KU-166-004

WWE: Annual 2022
A CENTUM BOOK 978-1-913865-72-6
Published in Great Britain by Centum Books Ltd
This edition published 2021
1 3 5 7 9 10 8 6 4 2

Centum Books Ltd, 20 Devon Square, Newton Abbot, Devon, TQ12 2HR, UK
9/10 Fenian St, Dublin 2, D02 RX24, Ireland
books@centumbooksltd.co.uk
CENTUM BOOKS Limited Reg. No. 07641486
A CIP catalogue record for this book is available from the British Library.
Printed in China.

THIS ANNUAL BELONGS TO:

centum

CONTENTS

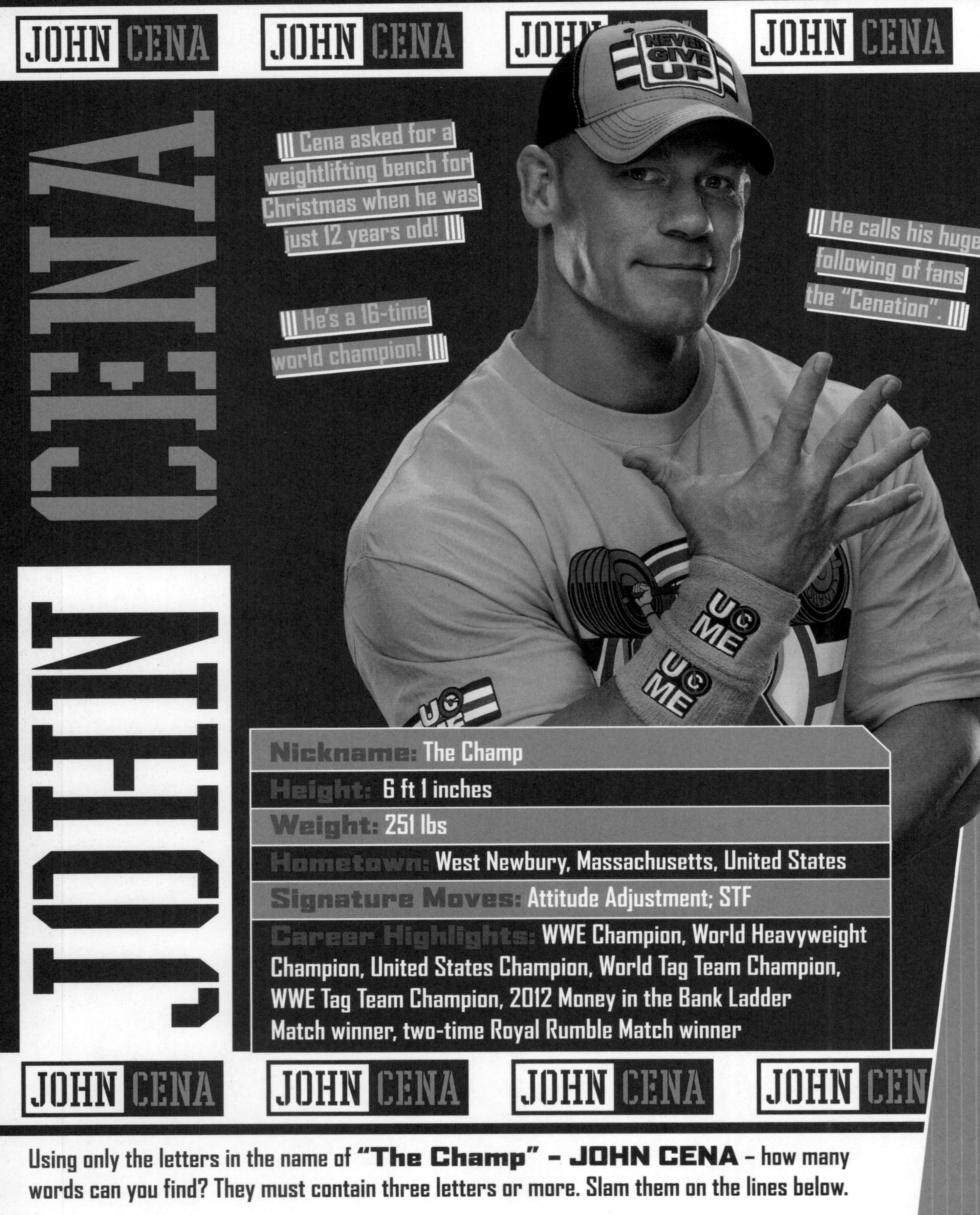
JOHN CENA
JOHN CENA
Cena asked for a weightlifting bench for Christmas when he was just 12 years old!
He's a 16-time world champion!
He calls his huge following of fans the "Cenation".
NEVER GIVE UP
U C ME

Nickname:	The Champ
Height:	6 ft 1 inches
Weight:	251 lbs
Hometown:	West Newbury, Massachusetts, United States
Signature Moves:	Attitude Adjustment; STF
Career Highlights:	WWE Champion, World Heavyweight Champion, United States Champion, World Tag Team Champion, WWE Tag Team Champion, 2012 Money in the Bank Ladder Match winner, two-time Royal Rumble Match winner

Using only the letters in the name of **"The Champ" – JOHN CENA** – how many words can you find? They must contain three letters or more. Slam them on the lines below.

CRACK THE CENA CODE

Listen up! This living legend of WWE has spoken many a wise word. Can you smash the code to reveal three unforgettable John Cena phrases?

KEY

A	B	C	D	E	F	G	H	I	J	K	L	M
1	2	3	4	5	6	7	8	9	10	11	12	13

N	O	P	Q	R	S	T	U	V	W	X	Y	Z
14	15	16	17	18	19	20	21	22	23	24	25	26

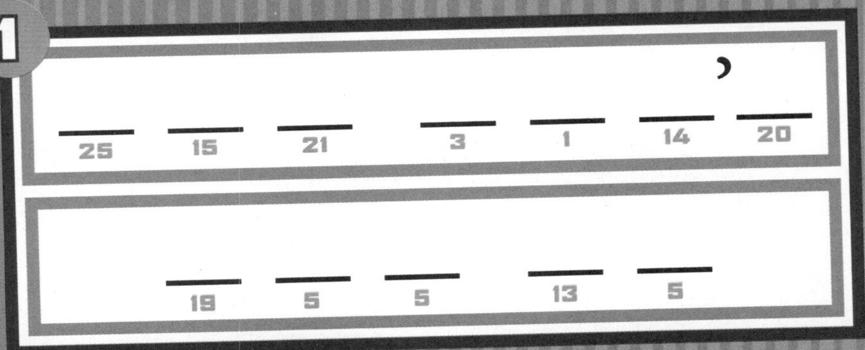

SLAMMIN' SILLIES
Q: What did John Cena say to his primary school teacher when she gave him his exam results?
A: You can't C me!
HA HA
JOHN CENA

2

8 21 19 20 12 5 ' 12 15 25 1 12 20 25 '

18 5 19 16 5 3 20

ANSWERS: ON PAGE 76

ROMAN REIGNS

Roman has a famous Superstar family. His cousin is The Rock! Other family members include The Usos, Rikishi, and The Wild Samoans.

Before becoming a WWE Superstar, Reigns played professional American football.

As a child Roman idolised Bret Hart and still thinks he's pretty cool today.

Nickname: Head of the Table

Height: 6 ft 3 inches

Weight: 265 lbs

Hometown: Pensacola, Florida, United States

Signature Moves: Spear; Superman Punch

Career Highlights: Universal Champion, WWE Champion, Intercontinental Champion, United States Champion, WWE Tag Team Champion, 2015 Royal Rumble Match winner, 2014 Superstar of the Year, Slammy Award winner

SPOT UP AND WIN!

There are 12 differences between these two pictures – **can you spot and circle them all?**

SLAMMIN' SILLIES
Q:
When does "The Fiend" need to take shelter?
A:
When it Reigns!
HA HA

There are 7 words hiding in this grid – can you find them?

– Wreck it and leave!

FLORIDA
PENSACOLA
REIGNS
ROMAN
SMACKDOWN
SPEAR
THE BIG DOG

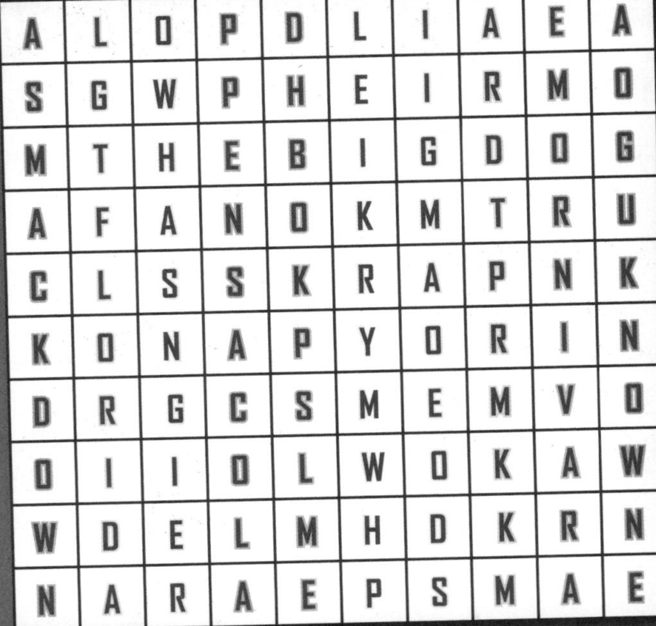

A	L	O	P	D	L	I	A	E	A
S	G	W	P	H	E	I	R	M	O
M	T	H	E	B	I	G	D	O	G
A	F	A	N	O	K	M	T	R	U
C	L	S	S	K	R	A	P	N	K
K	O	N	A	P	Y	O	R	I	N
D	R	G	C	S	M	E	M	V	O
O	I	I	O	L	W	O	K	A	W
W	D	E	L	M	H	D	K	R	N
N	A	R	A	E	P	S	M	A	E

ANSWERS: ON PAGE 76

BECKY LYNCH

Becky was the longest-running Raw Women's Champion in history, fending off challenges from many Superstars, including Sasha Banks and Lacey Evans, until her reign ended in May 2020.

She absolutely loves clowns and takes inspiration from them for her performances in the ring.

Nickname: The Man

Height: 5 ft 6 inches

Hometown: Dublin, Ireland

Signature Moves: Dis-arm-her; Man-handle Slam

Career Highlights: Raw Women's Champion, SmackDown Women's Champion, 2019 Women's Royal Rumble Match winner

She's The Man!

Copy the picture of the Raw Superstar into the empty grid, and throw down your best colours.

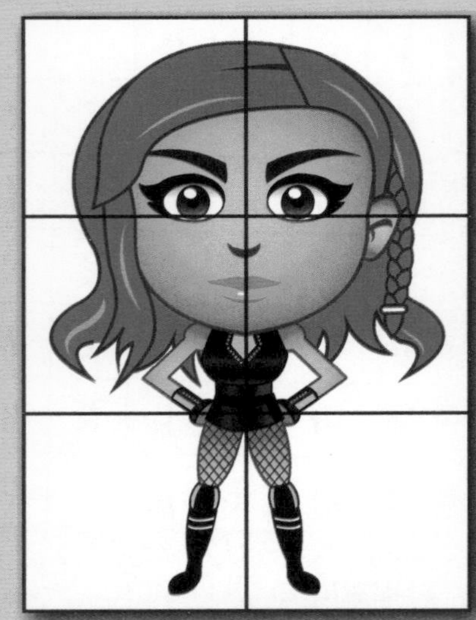

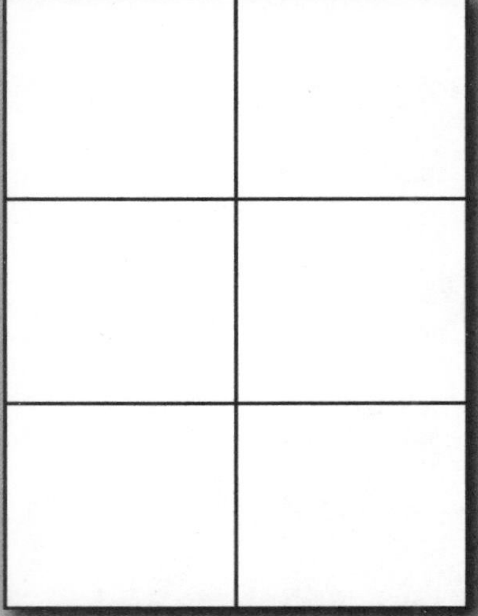

LYNCH THE WORDS

Search out 15 words in this Becky-themed puzzle.
Look up, down, forwards, backwards and diagonally.
Lynch them all!

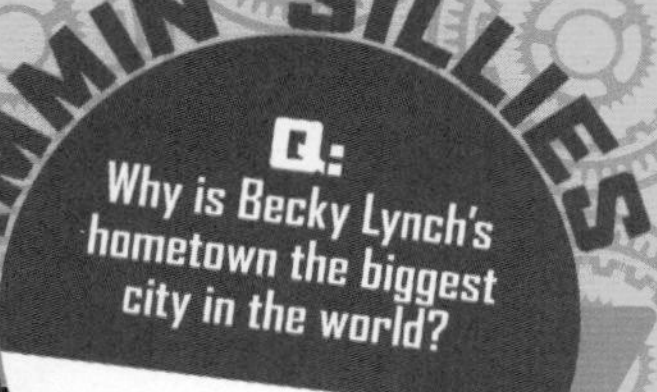

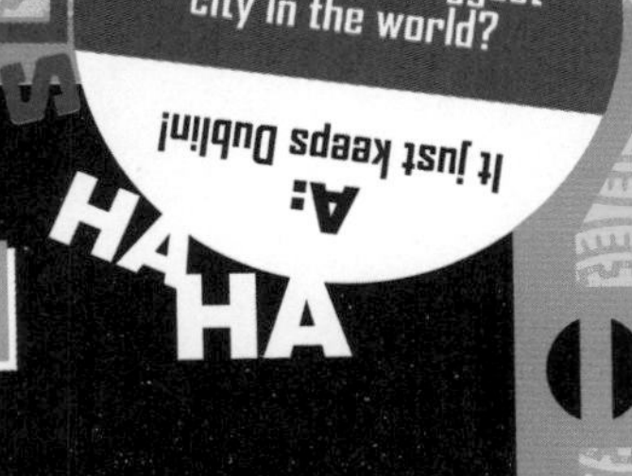

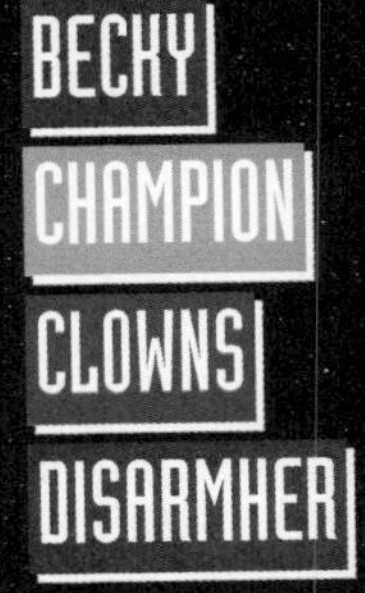

BECKY
CHAMPION
CLOWNS
DISARMHER
DUBLIN
IRELAND
LYNCH
MAN-HANDLE SLAM
RAW
ROYAL RUMBLE
SLAM
SMACKDOWN
SUPERSTAR
THE MAN
WRESTLEMANIA

SLAMMIN' SILLIES

Q: Why is Becky Lynch's hometown the biggest city in the world?

A: It just keeps Dublin!

HA HA HA

S	M	A	C	K	D	O	W	N	A	W	D	O	R	M
U	B	W	W	H	P	A	R	D	O	C	I	R	U	A
P	I	E	K	W	A	W	E	U	W	K	S	O	L	N
E	D	A	C	O	K	M	T	B	U	A	A	Y	L	H
R	L	I	D	K	L	A	P	L	K	O	R	A	S	A
S	O	R	K	P	Y	W	R	I	N	B	M	L	N	N
T	H	E	M	A	N	E	W	N	O	S	H	R	W	D
A	O	L	W	L	C	O	A	M	W	N	E	U	I	L
R	O	A	C	O	H	D	K	D	W	S	R	M	A	E
U	V	N	L	W	L	O	K	A	E	N	D	B	K	S
O	R	D	O	W	D	S	L	A	M	I	T	L	E	L
N	L	B	W	R	R	L	B	B	C	R	K	E	C	A
S	A	L	N	W	P	W	A	W	W	E	A	M	S	M
W	R	E	S	T	L	E	M	A	N	I	A	L	B	Y
U	E	H	I	M	Y	S	A	R	C	Y	O	T	A	L

ANSWERS: ON PAGE 76

CHARLOTTE FLAIR
CHARLOTTE FLAIR
CHARLOTTE FLAIR
CHARLOTTE FLAIR
Her father is WWE legend "Nature Boy" Ric Flair!
Charlotte is the most decorated female Superstar in WWE history.
She was an incredible volleyball player when she was younger. She won four championships with her college team!
CHARLOTTE FLAIR

Nickname: The Queen

Height: 5 ft 10 inches

Hometown: "The Queen City" – Charlotte, North Carolina, United States

Signature Moves: Figure-Eight Leglock; Natural Selection

Career Highlights: SmackDown Women's Champion, Raw Women's Champion, WWE Women's Champion, Divas Champion, 2020 Women's Royal Rumble Match winner, NXT Women's Champion, WWE Women's Tag Team Champion

Stun the world and work out these **slammin' scrambles!**

1. NEQUE ....

2. KECGLLO ....

3. BLOVELLALY ....

4. REANTU OYB ....

5. QUORENC ....

CONQUER WITH COLOUR

Add some Queen style flair to this page with your best colouring pens. **You were born to conquer!**

SLAMMIN' SILLIES
Q:
How did Asuka win the Women's Tag Team Championship?
A:
With Flair!
HA HA

CHARLOTTE FLAIR

ANSWERS: ON PAGE 76

THE ROCK

He's the son of a WWE Hall of Famer, Rocky Johnson.

Despite a hugely successful movie career, The Rock still returned to the ring in the main event of WrestleMania XXVIII against John Cena.

At university he studied criminology and physiology, earning degrees in both – he wanted to join the FBI!

Nickname: The Great One

Height: 6 ft 5 inches

Weight: 260 lbs

Hometown: Miami, Florida, United States

Signature Moves: Rock Bottom; The People's Elbow

Career Highlights: WWE Champion, Intercontinental Champion, World Tag Team Champion, 2000 Royal Rumble Match winner, WCW Champion

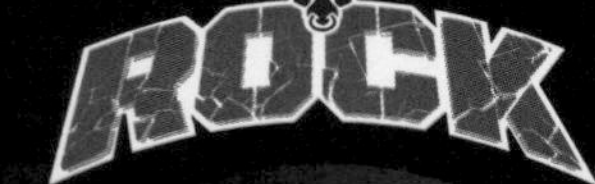

How many times can you see the word **"ROCK"** in this letter grid? Look up, down, diagonally, forwards and backwards. It doesn't matter how you do it – just **circle them all!**

R	O	C	K	R
O	O	R	C	O
C	K	C	O	R
K	C	R	K	O
K	O	R	K	C
C	R	O	C	K

WHICH IS THE GREAT ONE?

Only one of these silhouettes is the real Rock.
Can you find him? Just bring it!

CATCHPHRASE:
"IT DOESN'T MATTER WHAT YOUR NAME IS."

CATCHPHRASE:
"THE JABRONI-BEATIN', PIE-EATIN', TRAILBLAZIN' PEOPLE'S CHAMP!"

CATCHPHRASE:
"CAN YOU SMELL WHAT THE ROCK IS COOKING?"

ANSWERS: ON PAGE 76

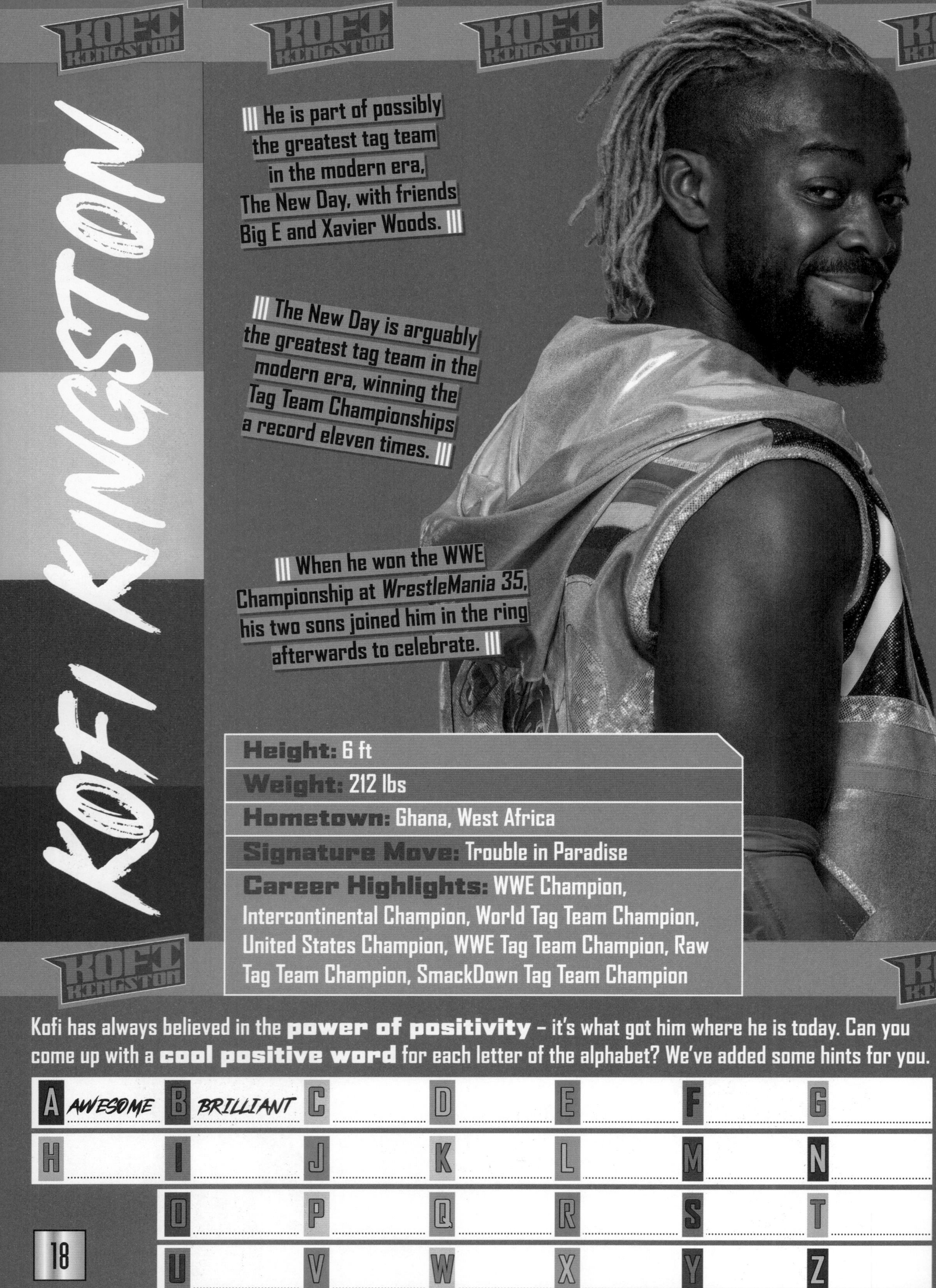

KOFI KINGSTON

||| He is part of possibly the greatest tag team in the modern era, The New Day, with friends Big E and Xavier Woods. |||

||| The New Day is arguably the greatest tag team in the modern era, winning the Tag Team Championships a record eleven times. |||

||| When he won the WWE Championship at *WrestleMania 35*, his two sons joined him in the ring afterwards to celebrate. |||

Height: 6 ft

Weight: 212 lbs

Hometown: Ghana, West Africa

Signature Move: Trouble in Paradise

Career Highlights: WWE Champion, Intercontinental Champion, World Tag Team Champion, United States Champion, WWE Tag Team Champion, Raw Tag Team Champion, SmackDown Tag Team Champion

Kofi has always believed in the **power of positivity** – it's what got him where he is today. Can you come up with a **cool positive word** for each letter of the alphabet? We've added some hints for you.

A AWESOME	B BRILLIANT	C	D	E	F	G
H	I	J	K	L	M	N
	O	P	Q	R	S	T
	U	V	W	X	Y	Z

THE POWER OF POSITIVITY

CATCHPHRASE:
"NEW DAY ROCKS!"

Use some of that Kofi power and **write your biggest dreams** on this page. Then draw your biggest dream underneath. Think positive and **make it happen!**

MY BIGGEST DREAM IS:

THIS IS HOW I'M GOING TO MAKE IT HAPPEN:

CATCHPHRASE:
"BOOM. BOOM. BOOM!"

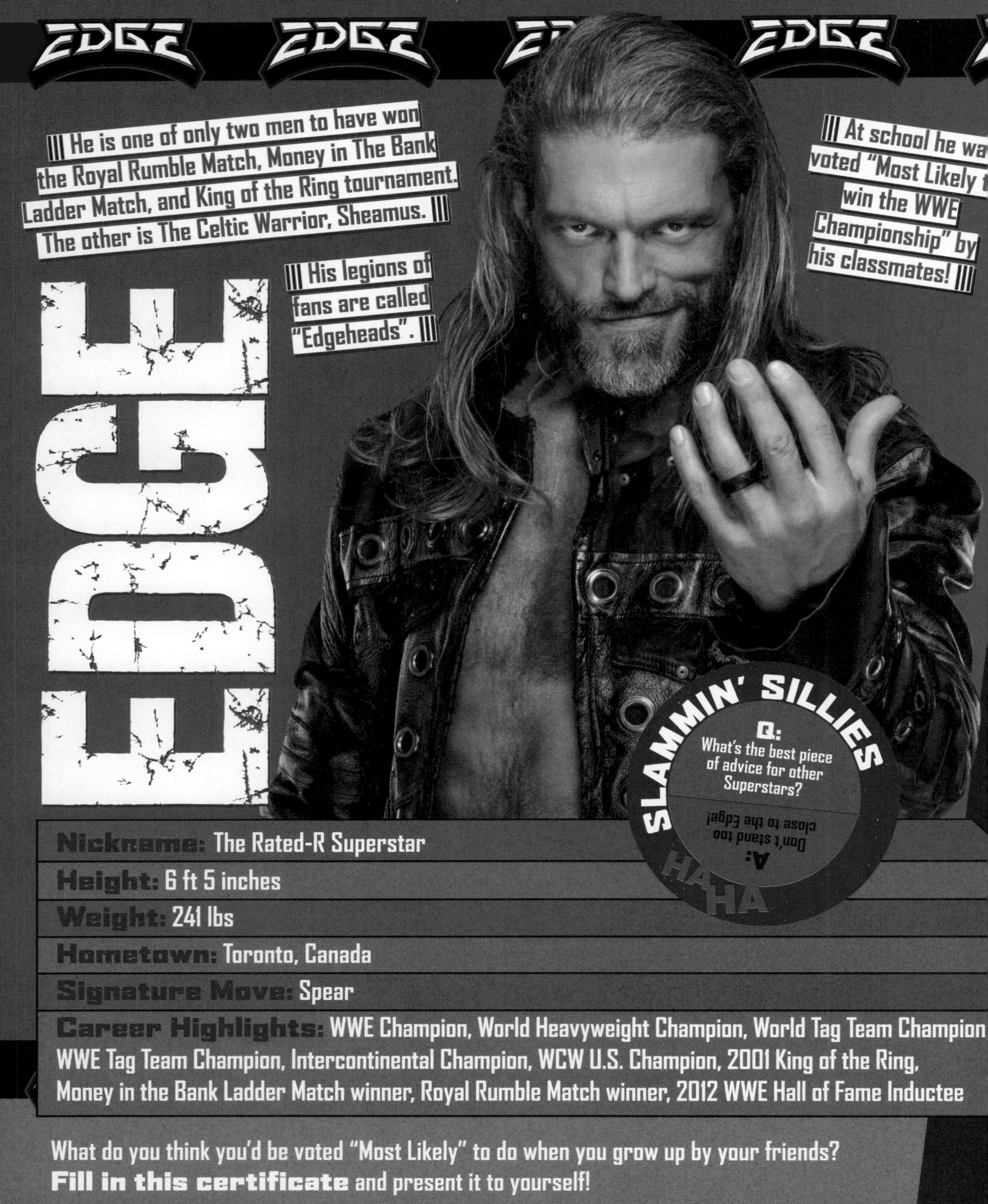

He is one of only two men to have won the Royal Rumble Match, Money in The Bank Ladder Match, and King of the Ring tournament. The other is The Celtic Warrior, Sheamus.

At school he wa voted "Most Likely t win the WWE Championship" by his classmates!

His legions of fans are called "Edgeheads".

EDGE

SLAMMIN' SILLIES

Q: What's the best piece of advice for other Superstars?

A: Don't stand too close to the Edge!

HA HA

Nickname: The Rated-R Superstar

Height: 6 ft 5 inches

Weight: 241 lbs

Hometown: Toronto, Canada

Signature Move: Spear

Career Highlights: WWE Champion, World Heavyweight Champion, World Tag Team Champion WWE Tag Team Champion, Intercontinental Champion, WCW U.S. Champion, 2001 King of the Ring, Money in the Bank Ladder Match winner, Royal Rumble Match winner, 2012 WWE Hall of Fame Inductee

What do you think you'd be voted "Most Likely" to do when you grow up by your friends? **Fill in this certificate** and present it to yourself!

Name ______________________________

Has been voted most likely to ______________________________

Because ______________________________

DO YOU KNOW ME?

"You think you know me!" is one of Edge's famous phrases to wind up his opponents. But do you really know him? Cover up his profile on the opposite page (no cheating!), then **put yourself to the test with this Edge quiz.**

1. WHAT IS EDGE'S REAL NAME?

   ____

2. DOES HE APPEAR ON SMACKDOWN OR RAW?

   ____

3. WHAT YEAR WAS HE BORN?

   ____

4. WHAT IS HIS SIGNATURE MOVE?

   ____

5. WHAT COUNTRY IS HE FROM?

   ____

6. WHAT BAND DID HE GROW UP LISTENING TO?

   ____

7. HOW TALL IS HE?

   ____

8. WHAT STRINGED INSTRUMENT DOES EDGE COLLECT?

   ____

9. WHAT MATERIAL ARE HIS LONG JACKETS MADE FROM?

   ____

10. WHAT FORCED EDGE TO RETIRE IN 2011?

    ____

WHOSE BOOTS?

Every Superstar has a signature style, and their footwear is iconic. Can you work out **whose boots are whose** from these pictures? Write the Superstar name under each pair.

1

2

3

4

?

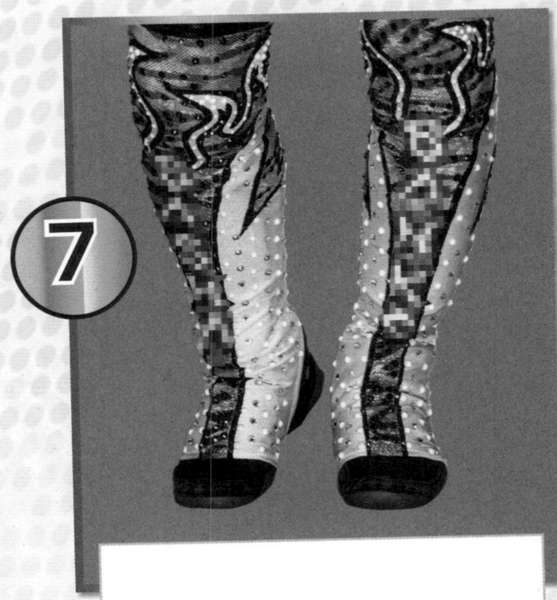

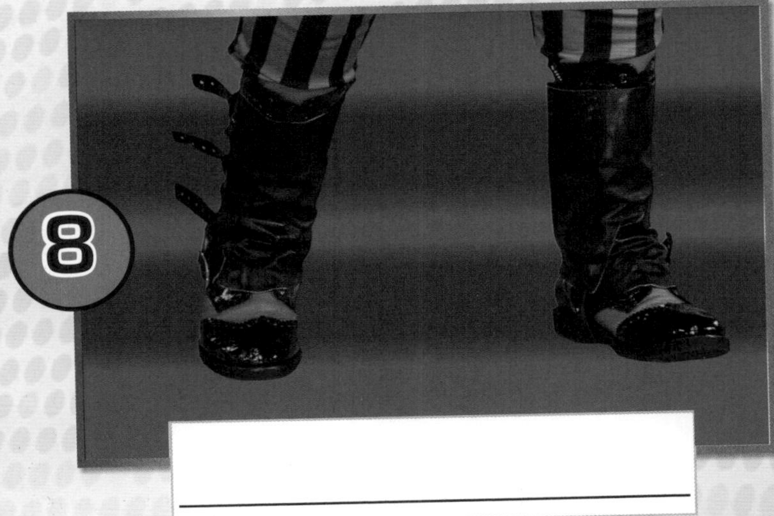

?

DESIGN YOUR OWN BOOTS!

If you were a WWE Superstar, what footwear would you rock into the ring?
Design them here!

ANSWERS: ON PAGE 76

KEEP IT IN THE FAMILY

WWE features some formidably talented famous families, with sons, daughters and cousins following in the footsteps of their Superstar relatives. Can you **match up** the four pairs of related stars? **Write your answers in the box.**

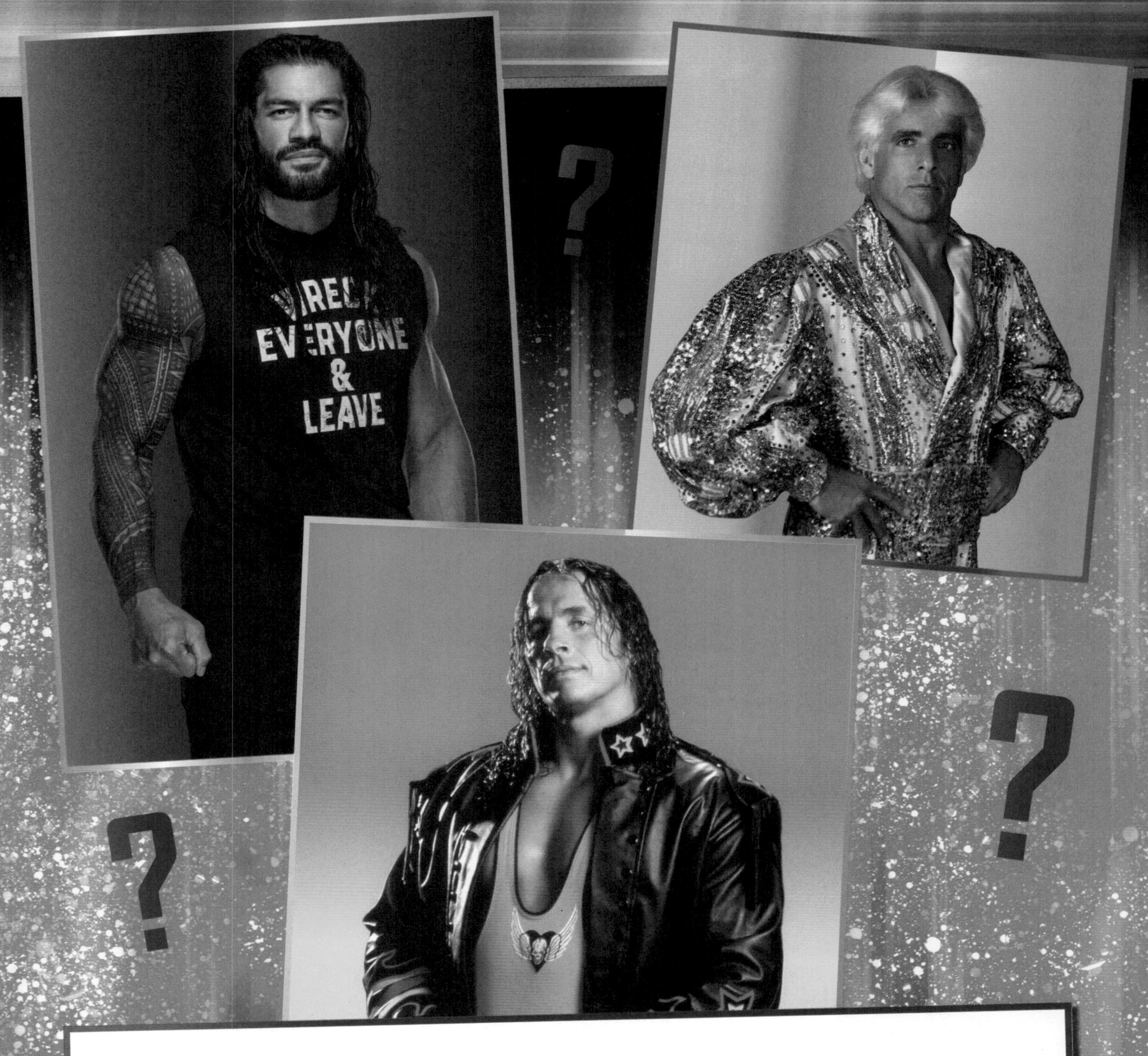

___ _____ & __________ _____

[father and daughter]

___ ____ & _____ ______

[cousins]

____ ____ & ________

[uncle and niece]

ANSWERS: ON PAGE 76

Drew started training to become a WWE Superstar when he was just 15 years old!

He defeated Brock Lesnar at the main event of WrestleMania 36 to capture his first WWE Championship.

He has a master's degree in criminology from Glasgow Caledonian University.

Nickname: The Scottish Warrior

Height: 6 ft 5 inches

Weight: 265 lbs

Hometown: Ayr, Scotland

Signature Move: Claymore

Career Highlights: WWE Champion, 2020 Men's Royal Rumble Match winner, Intercontinental Champion, WWE Tag Team Champion, Raw Tag Team Champion, NXT Champion, Raw's Gold Medal of Excellence

McIntyre might not like maths, but do you? The number in each square below is equal to the sum of the numbers in the circles on either side of it. **Fill in the missing numbers!**

TALK LESS, CLAYMORE!

Drew is never afraid to drop any opponent with his signature move. **Help him find the path to his rival through the grid** by following the word **CLAYMORE** three times.

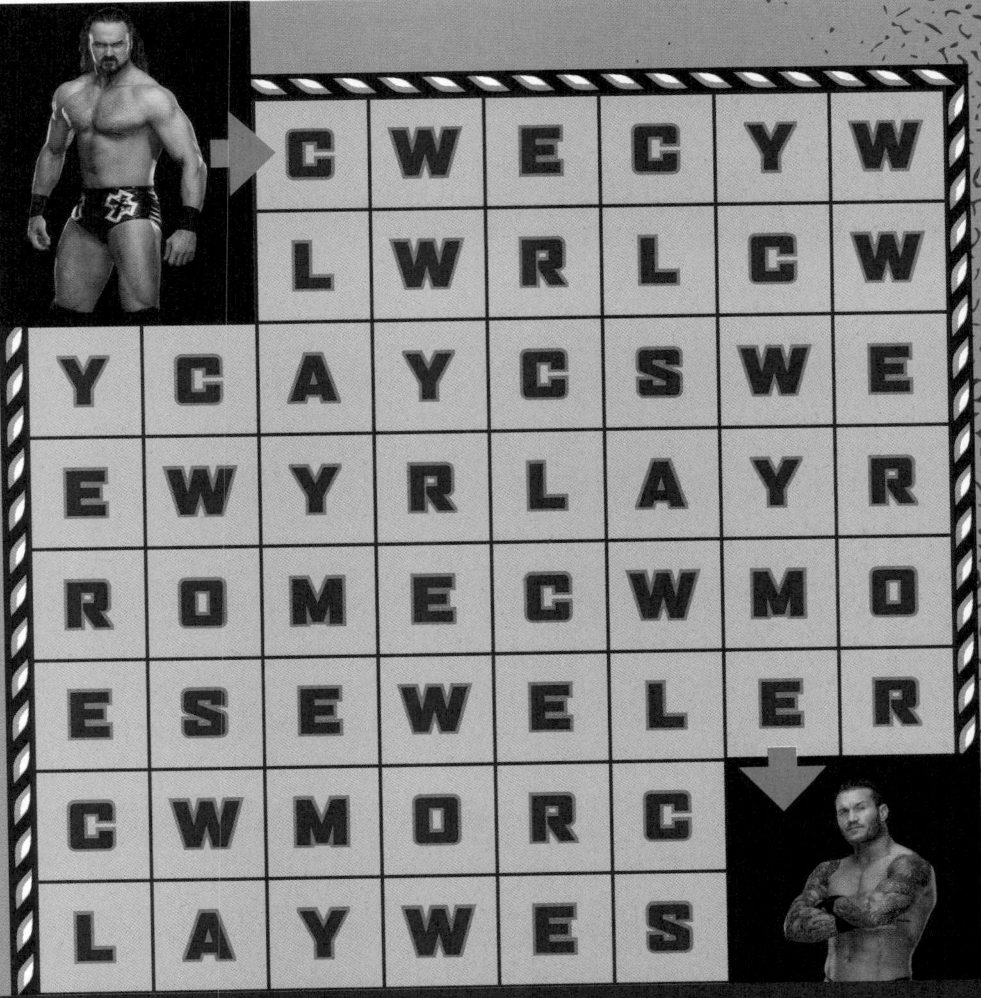

C W E C Y W
L W R L C W
Y C A Y C S W E
E W Y R L A Y R
R O M E C W M O
E S E W E L E R
C W M O R C
L A Y W E S

His catchphrase might say "talk less", but McIntyre has said a few famous things in his time. Which two of these do you think are genuine quotes from the Scottish Warrior? **Put a tick next to your answers.**

1. "I am happy to do anything that comes my way, and I will always do my best in anything that presents itself." ☐
2. "Failure's not an option. It's just a step." ☐
3. "All success begins with self-discipline. It starts with you." ☐
4. "I want to inspire people and show people no matter what happens, no matter how much you get knocked down, you can pick yourself up. Just keep pushing forward, keep being positive." ☐

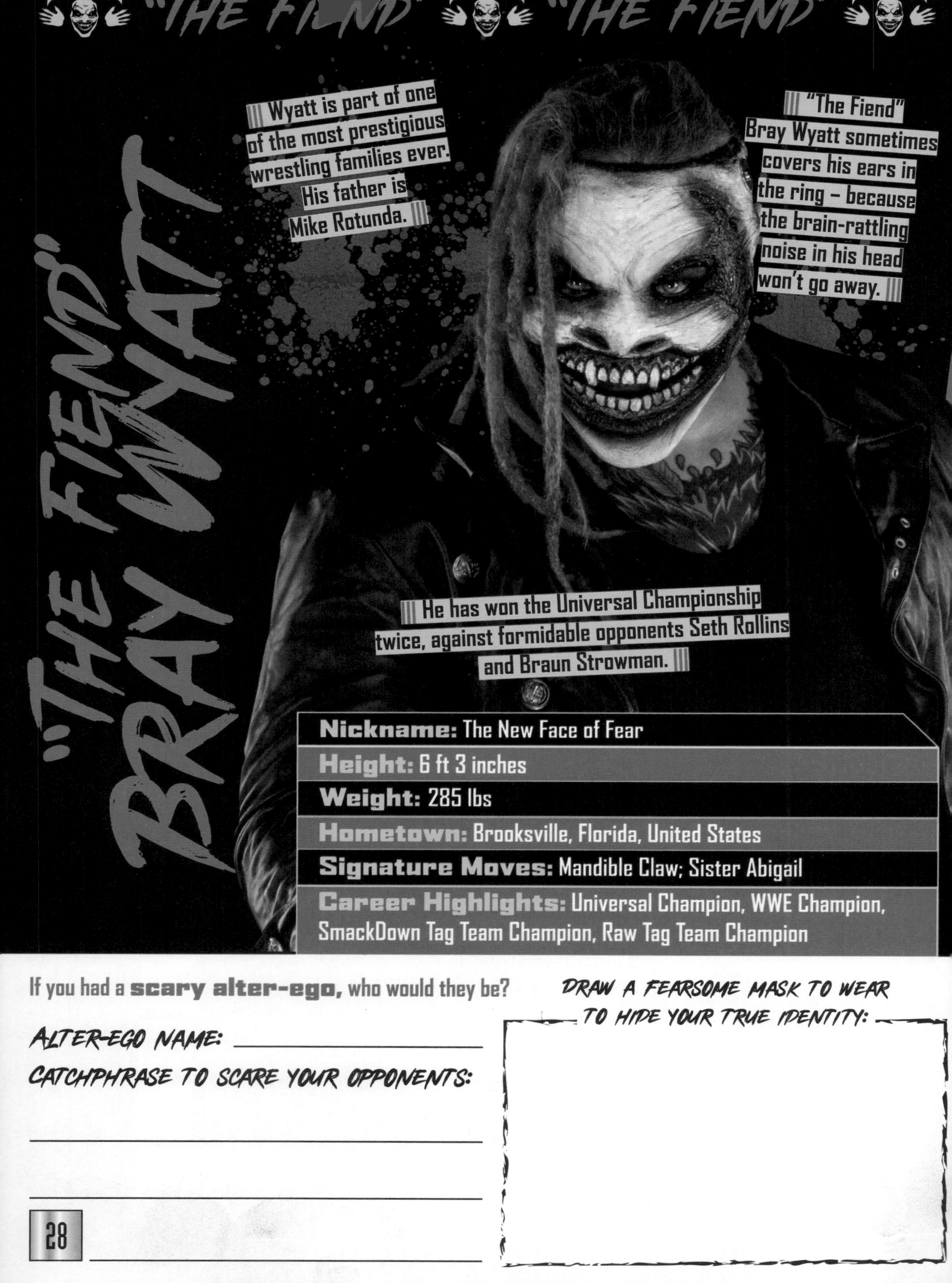

"THE FIEND" "THE FIEND"
"THE FIEND" BRAY WYATT
Wyatt is part of one of the most prestigious wrestling families ever. His father is Mike Rotunda.
"The Fiend" Bray Wyatt sometimes covers his ears in the ring – because the brain-rattling noise in his head won't go away.
He has won the Universal Championship twice, against formidable opponents Seth Rollins and Braun Strowman.

Nickname: The New Face of Fear

Height: 6 ft 3 inches

Weight: 285 lbs

Hometown: Brooksville, Florida, United States

Signature Moves: Mandible Claw; Sister Abigail

Career Highlights: Universal Champion, WWE Champion, SmackDown Tag Team Champion, Raw Tag Team Champion

If you had a **scary alter-ego,** who would they be?

ALTER-EGO NAME: ____________________

CATCHPHRASE TO SCARE YOUR OPPONENTS:

____

____

____

DRAW A FEARSOME MASK TO WEAR TO HIDE YOUR TRUE IDENTITY:

SUPERSTAR SCRAMBLE

Quote: "I will take my rightful place among the gods as the new Face of Fear."

Can you **unscramble the names** of The Fiend's biggest ring rivals?

Quote: "I have been the answer all along."

1 HONJ AENC

_ _ _ _ _ _ _ _ _ _ _ _ _

Quote: "Let me in!"

2 NORMA GIRENS

_ _ _ _ _ _ _ _ _ _ _ _

3 NEKA

_ _ _ _

4 TEHS LORINLS

_ _ _ _ _ _ _ _ _ _ _

5 NARUB MTORSANW

_ _ _ _ _ _ _ _ _ _ _ _ _

6 DRANY TOORN

_ _ _ _ _ _ _ _ _ _

7 JA LETSSY

_ _

_ _ _ _ _ _

8 VEINK NOEWS

_ _ _ _ _ _ _ _ _ _

ANSWERS: ON PAGE 76

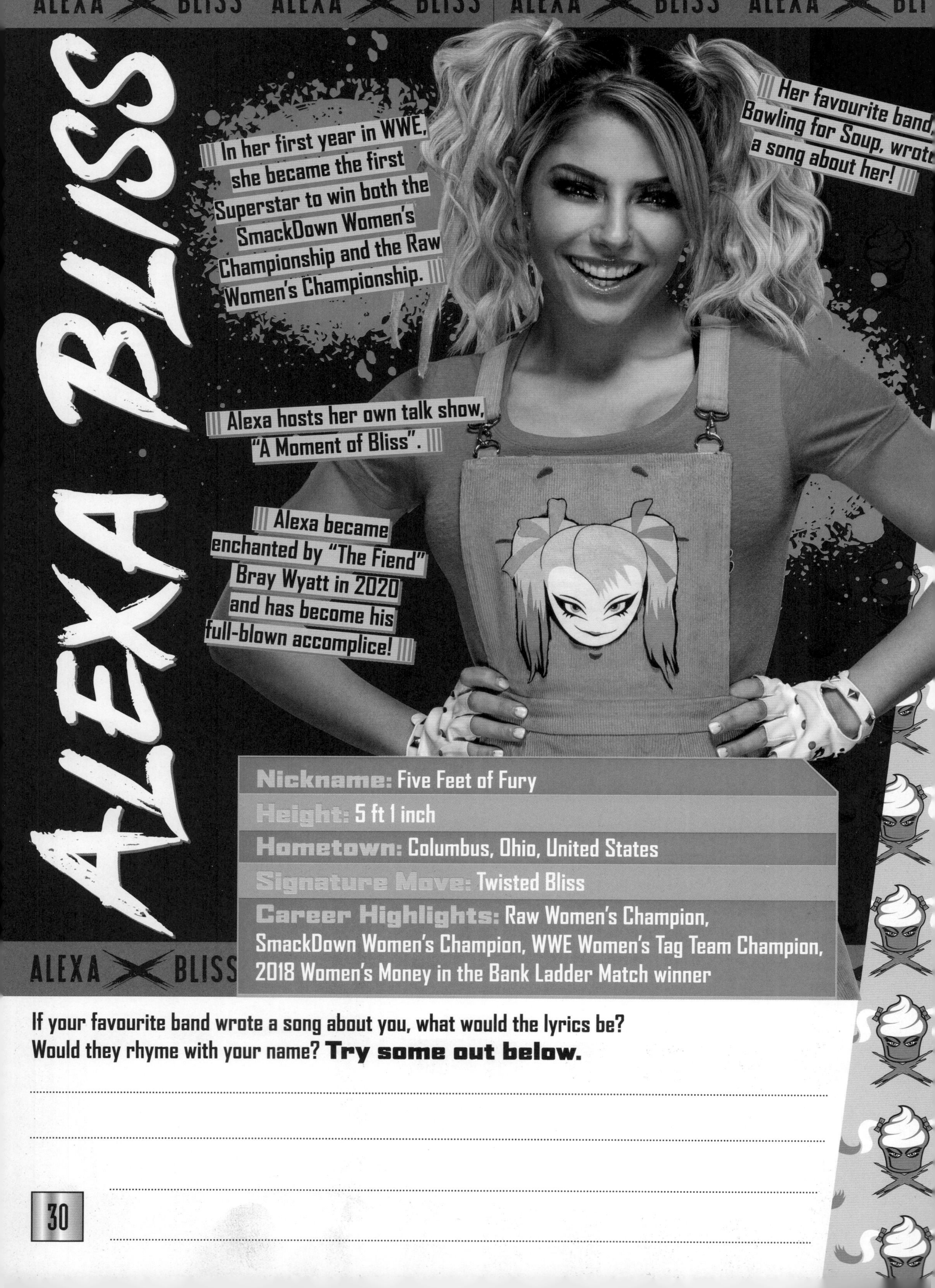

ALEXA BLISS

In her first year in WWE, she became the first Superstar to win both the SmackDown Women's Championship and the Raw Women's Championship.

Her favourite band, Bowling for Soup, wrote a song about her!

Alexa hosts her own talk show, "A Moment of Bliss".

Alexa became enchanted by "The Fiend" Bray Wyatt in 2020 and has become his full-blown accomplice!

ALEXA BLISS

Nickname: Five Feet of Fury
Height: 5 ft 1 inch
Hometown: Columbus, Ohio, United States
Signature Move: Twisted Bliss
Career Highlights: Raw Women's Champion, SmackDown Women's Champion, WWE Women's Tag Team Champion, 2018 Women's Money in the Bank Ladder Match winner

If your favourite band wrote a song about you, what would the lyrics be? Would they rhyme with your name? **Try some out below.**

....

....

....

....

DOUBLE BLISS

Can you create some Alexa-style awesomeness by **creating a double of her blissful badge** and matching the colours, too?

SLAMMIN' SILLIES

Q: What kind of match is hard to get out of the box?

A: A WWE match!

HA HA

BIG E

In 2020, Big E joined Friday Night SmackDown, while Kofi and Xavier were drafted to Raw.

He's so strong, he can deadlift a small car!

Big E broke the bench press record at John Cena's gym back in 2011 lifting an impressive 575 pounds. Now that's some serious strength!

Height: 5 ft 11 inches

Weight: 285 lbs

Hometown: Tampa, Florida, United States

Signature moves: Big Ending; Midnight Hour

Career Highlights: Intercontinental Champion, Raw Tag Team Champion, SmackDown Tag Team Champion, WWE Tag Team Champion, NXT Champion

Every column, row and mini-grid in this puzzle should contain the letters **SMACKDOWN**. Can you throw down the missing letters to complete the grid? **Don't rush the win – think logically!**

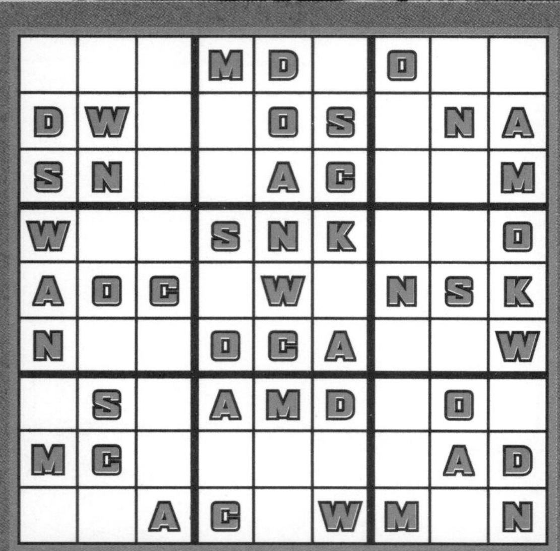

			M	D		O		
D	W			O	S		N	A
S	N			A	C			M
W			S	N	K			O
A	O	C		W		N	S	K
N			O	C	A			W
	S		A	M	D		O	
M	C						A	D
		A	C		W	M		N

SLAMMIN' SILLIES
Q: Why is Big E good at maths?
A: Because he's the Master of the Five Count!
HA HA

THINK BIG E

Like the ring after Big E has conquered his opponents, only the Es are left standing in these words. Can you work out what the words are and **add the missing letters?**

1. WHAT DO WE CALL ALL THE AWESOME PERFORMERS IN **WWE?**

_ _ _ E _ _ _ _ _ _

2. WHAT **WWE** TEAM WAS BIG A PART OF WITH KOFI KINGSTON AND XAVIER WOODS?

_ _ E   _ E _   _ _ _

3. WHAT IS ONE OF BIG 'S SIGNATURE MOVES?

_ _ _ _   E _ _ _ _ _ _ _

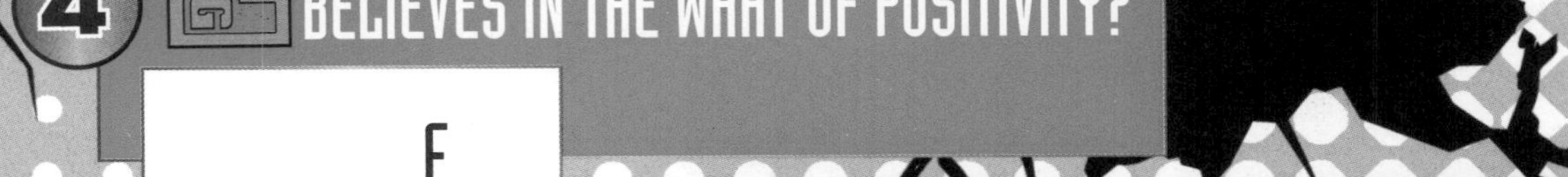

4. BIG BELIEVES IN THE WHAT OF POSITIVITY?

_ _ _ E _

5. **THE NEW DAY** IS A FAMOUS WHAT?

_ _ _   _ E _ _

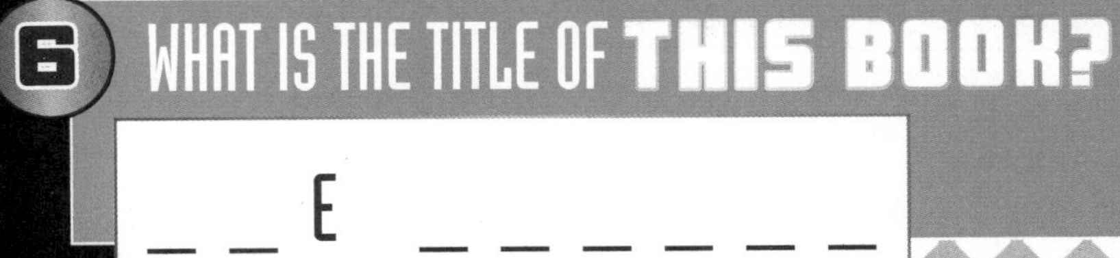

6. WHAT IS THE TITLE OF **THIS BOOK?**

_ _ E   _ _ _ _ _ _ _ _

7. WHAT COUNTRY IS BIG FROM?

_ _ _ _ E _   _ _ _ _ E _

ANSWERS: ON PAGE 76

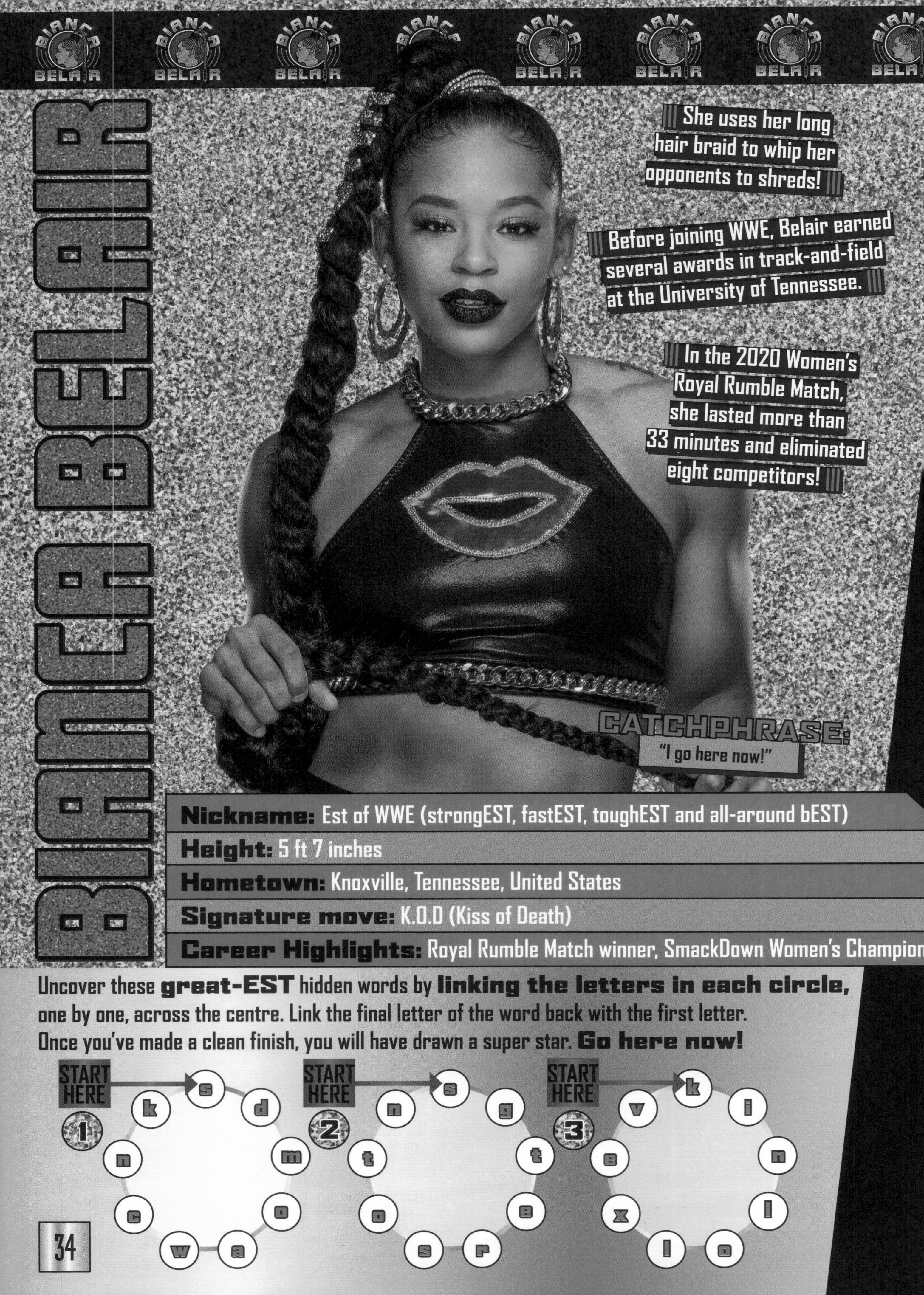
BIANCA BELAIR
BIANCA BELAIR
She uses her long hair braid to whip her opponents to shreds!
Before joining WWE, Belair earned several awards in track-and-field at the University of Tennessee.
In the 2020 Women's Royal Rumble Match, she lasted more than 33 minutes and eliminated eight competitors!
CATCHPHRASE:
"I go here now!"
Nickname: Est of WWE (strongEST, fastEST, toughEST and all-around bEST)
Height: 5 ft 7 inches
Hometown: Knoxville, Tennessee, United States
Signature move: K.O.D (Kiss of Death)
Career Highlights: Royal Rumble Match winner, SmackDown Women's Champion
Uncover these **great-EST** hidden words by **linking the letters in each circle,** one by one, across the centre. Link the final letter of the word back with the first letter. Once you've made a clean finish, you will have drawn a super star. **Go here now!**
START HERE
1
s d m o a w c n k
START HERE
2
s g t e r s o t n
START HERE
3
k i n l o l x e v

TRUEST OR FALSEST?

How much do you know about this greatEST Superstar?

Cover up her profile on the previous page (only some of the answers are there), then choose **"TRUE"** or **"FALSE"** for the statements below by circling your answer.

1. BIANCA IS FROM FLORIDA. **TRUE** **FALSE**
2. SHE TAUNTS HER OPPONENTS WITH THE WORDS "I GO HERE NOW". **TRUE** **FALSE**
3. BEFORE JOINING WWE, SHE WAS AN AMAZING TRACK-AND-FIELD ATHLETE AT HER UNIVERSITY. **TRUE** **FALSE**
4. SHE IS OVER 6 FEET TALL. **TRUE** **FALSE**
5. SHE WON THE WOMEN'S ROYAL RUMBLE MATCH IN 2021. **TRUE** **FALSE**
6. SHE IS RIC FLAIR'S DAUGHTER. **TRUE** **FALSE**
7. AT *WRESTLEMANIA 36*, SHE LENT A HELPING HAND TO TAG TEAM THE STREET PROFITS. **TRUE** **FALSE**
8. HER SIGNATURE MOVE IS THE CLAYMORE. **TRUE** **FALSE**

ANSWERS: ON PAGE 76

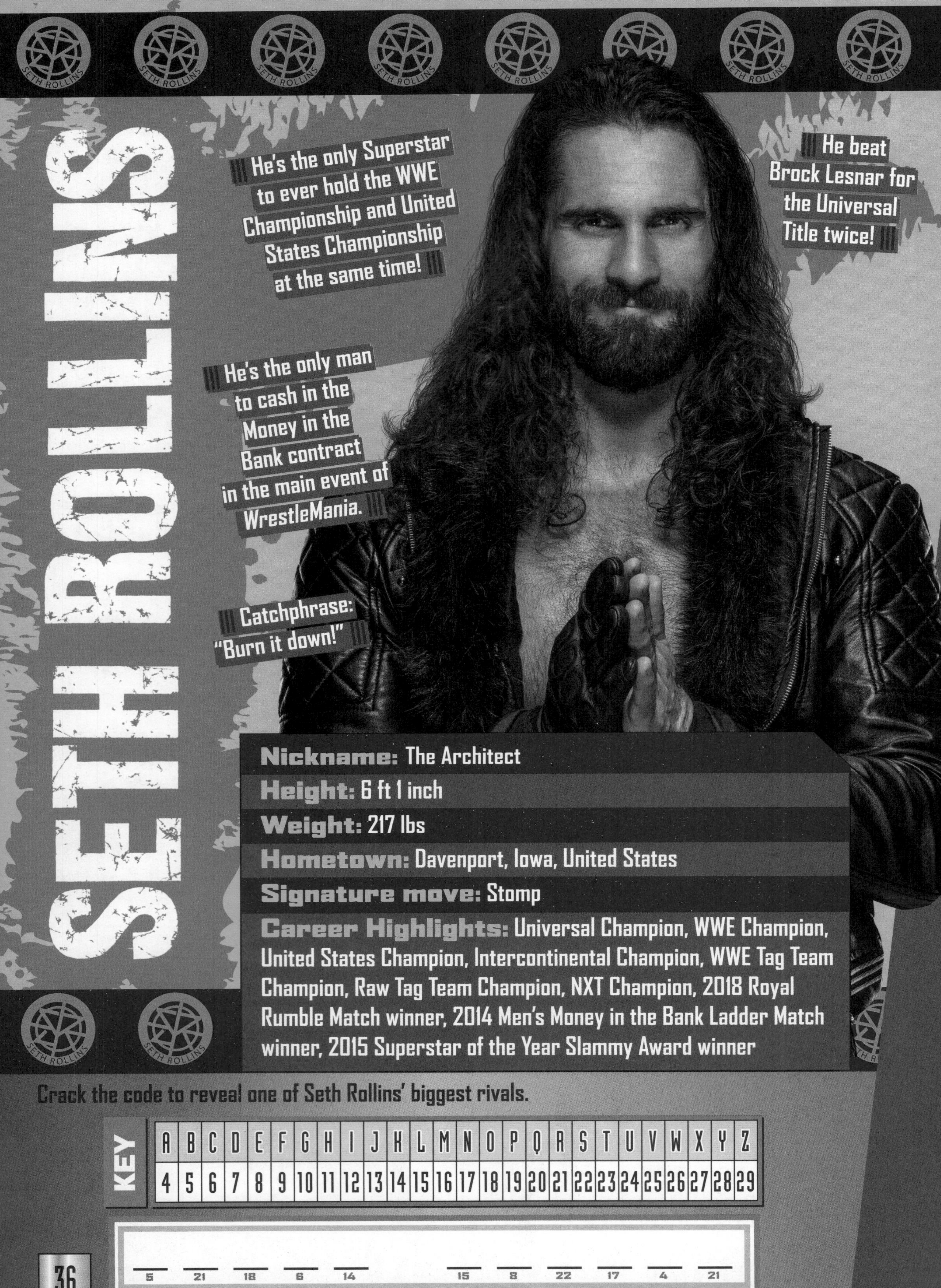

SETH ROLLINS
He's the only Superstar to ever hold the WWE Championship and United States Championship at the same time!
He beat Brock Lesnar for the Universal Title twice!
He's the only man to cash in the Money in the Bank contract in the main event of WrestleMania.
Catchphrase: "Burn it down!"

Nickname: The Architect

Height: 6 ft 1 inch

Weight: 217 lbs

Hometown: Davenport, Iowa, United States

Signature move: Stomp

Career Highlights: Universal Champion, WWE Champion, United States Champion, Intercontinental Champion, WWE Tag Team Champion, Raw Tag Team Champion, NXT Champion, 2018 Royal Rumble Match winner, 2014 Men's Money in the Bank Ladder Match winner, 2015 Superstar of the Year Slammy Award winner

Crack the code to reveal one of Seth Rollins' biggest rivals.

KEY	A	B	C	D	E	F	G	H	I	J	K	L	M	N	O	P	Q	R	S	T	U	V	W	X	Y	Z
	4	5	6	7	8	9	10	11	12	13	14	15	16	17	18	19	20	21	22	23	24	25	26	27	28	29

__ __ __ __ __   __ __ __ __ __ __

5 21 18 6 14   15 8 22 17 4 21

SLAY THE SEARCH

"Beast Slayer" is another of Seth's awesome nicknames. Can you slay this beast of a wordsearch and **find 15 words** related to the Slayer himself?

- ARCHITECT
- SLAYER
- CHAMPION
- DAVENPORT
- IOWA
- MESSIAH
- MONEY IN THE BANK
- ROLLINS
- SAVIOR
- SETH
- SMACKDOWN
- STOMP
- THE SHIELD
- UNIVERSAL
- WRESTLEMANIA

SLAMMIN' SILLIES

Q: Why did The Architect end up at the bottom of the hill?

A: He just kept Rollin!

HA HA

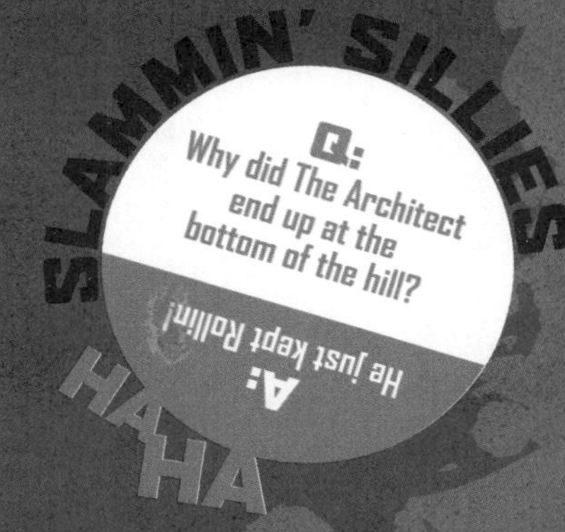

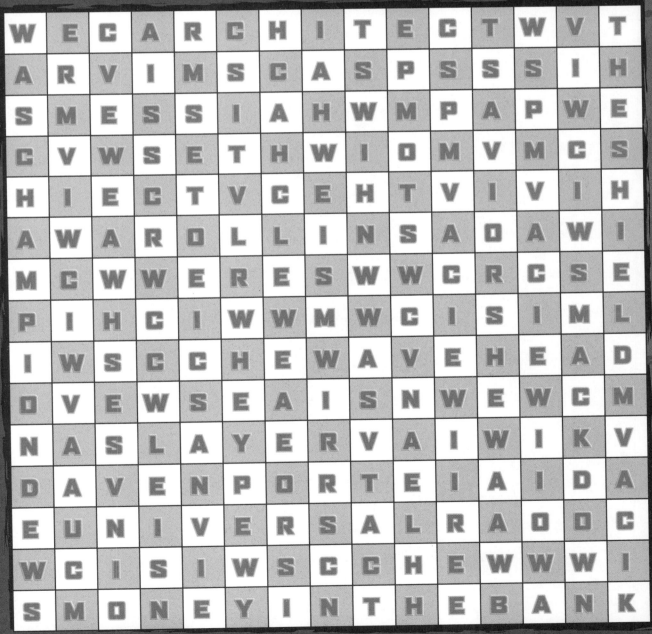

W	E	C	A	R	C	H	I	T	E	C	T	W	V	T
A	R	V	I	M	S	C	A	S	P	S	S	S	I	H
S	M	E	S	S	I	A	H	W	M	P	A	P	W	E
C	V	W	S	E	T	H	W	I	O	M	V	M	C	S
H	I	E	C	T	V	C	E	H	T	V	I	V	I	H
A	W	A	R	O	L	L	I	N	S	A	O	A	W	I
M	C	W	W	E	R	E	S	W	W	C	R	C	S	E
P	I	H	C	I	W	W	M	W	C	I	S	I	M	L
I	W	S	C	C	H	E	W	A	V	E	H	E	A	D
O	V	E	W	S	E	A	I	S	N	W	E	W	C	M
N	A	S	L	A	Y	E	R	V	A	I	W	I	K	V
D	A	V	E	N	P	O	R	T	E	I	A	I	D	A
E	U	N	I	V	E	R	S	A	L	R	A	O	O	C
W	C	I	S	I	W	S	C	C	H	E	W	W	W	I
S	M	O	N	E	Y	I	N	T	H	E	B	A	N	K

ANSWERS: ON PAGE 76

LEGIT BOSS
SASHA BANKS
She was one of the first women to compete in a major NXT match!
She teamed up with Bayley and they became the first WWE Women's Tag Team Champions.
Sasha eventually defeated her former best friend Bayley to win her first SmackDown Women's Championship in a fierce Hell in a Cell Match.
Nickname: The Boss
Height: 5 ft 5 inches
Hometown: Boston, Massachusetts, United States
Signature move: Bank Statement
Career Highlights: SmackDown Women's Champion, Raw Women's Champion, WWE Women's Champion, WWE Women's Tag Team Champion, NXT Women's Champion

BOSS THE DIFFERENCE

Can you spot and circle 10 differences in the second picture below?

Spot like a boss!

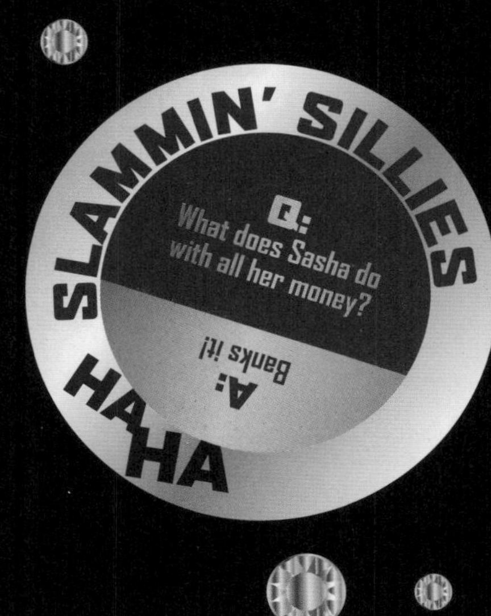

SLAMMIN' SILLIES
Q: What does Sasha do with all her money?
A: Banks it!
HA HA

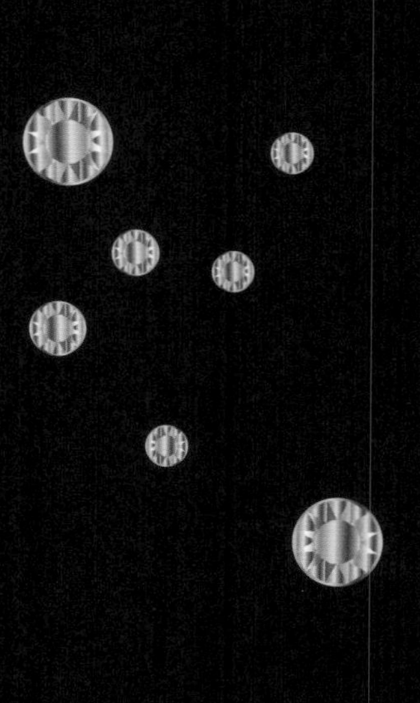

Imagine your own ultimate tag team!

Which friend would you team up with? ______________________

Why would they make the best companion in the ring?______________________

____

Your Tag Team name: ______________________

ANSWERS: ON PAGE 76

"THE ROCK" CAKES

Snacks are essential while watching the latest episodes of WWE action. Bake and share these simple rock cakes and all your friends will be calling you **"The Great One"**.

Preparation time: less than 30 mins
Cooking time: 15 to 20 mins
Makes: 12

INGREDIENTS

- **225g (8oz)** self-raising flour
- **75g (2.5oz)** caster sugar
- **1 teaspoon** baking powder
- **125g (4.5oz)** unsalted butter, cut into cubes
- **150g (5.5oz)** dried fruit
- **1** free-range egg
- **1 tablespoon** milk
- **2 teaspoons** vanilla extract

METHOD

1 Ask an adult to turn the oven on to 180ºC (160ºC Fan/Gas 4) to get it warmed up. Get your baking tray ready by lining it with baking parchment.

2 Mix the flour, sugar and baking powder in a large bowl, then rub in the cubed butter with your fingers until the mixture looks like breadcrumbs. Now stir in the dried fruit.

In a separate bowl, beat the egg, milk and vanilla extract together.

Now add the egg mixture to the dry ingredients and stir with a spoon until the mixture joins together as a thick, lumpy dough. Add a teaspoon more milk if needed to make the mixture stick together.

Place ping-pong-ball-sized dollops of the mixture onto the prepared baking tray, leaving a good amount of space between them, as they will flatten and spread out to double their size in the oven.

Bake for 15–20 minutes, until they look golden-brown. Ask an adult to take them out of the oven and place them on a wire rack to cool down before you eat them.

CAN YOU SMELL WHAT

THE ROCK

IS COOKIN'

THE ULTIMATE WWE QUIZ

How much do you really know about the WWE Universe? Test yourself then your friends with this ultimate quiz. **Circle your answer for each question.**

1 What is the name of the Friday night WWE television show?

Raw
SmackDown
NXT
WrestleMania

2 The Tombstone is a signature move of which legendary Superstar?

The Rock
Ultimate Warrior
Undertaker
Bret "Hit Man" Hart

3 What country is Becky Lynch from?

Ireland
Scotland
England
Canada

4 Who was the first person to become WWE Universal Champion?

Edge
"Stone Cold" Steve Austin
John Cena
Finn Bálor

What is the name of the Monday night WWE television show?

- Raw
- SmackDown
- NXT
- WrestleMania

Which Superstar is known as "The Man"?

- John Cena
- Roman Reigns
- Becky Lynch
- Sasha Banks

7

Which Superstar is cousin to Dwayne "The Rock" Johnson?

- Charlotte Flair
- Edge
- Bianca Belair
- Roman Reigns

What is "The Scottish Warrior" Drew McIntyre's signature move?

- Claymore
- Mandible Claw
- Big Ending
- Stomp

9

"The Fiend" is the alter-ego of which Superstar?

- Asuka
- Bray Wyatt
- Bret "Hit Man" Hart
- Alexa Bliss

Who was the first Superstar to ever escape The Rock's finisher move, The Rock Bottom?

- Ric Flair
- Shawn Michaels
- "Stone Cold" Steve Austin
- Randy Savage

ANSWERS: ON PAGE 76

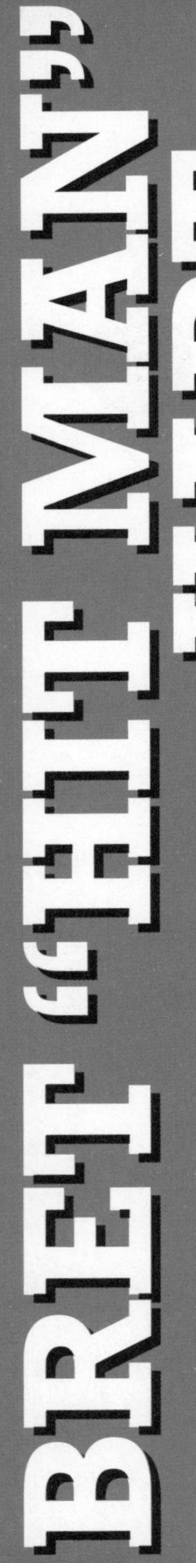

Hart won his first WWE Championship in a non-televised live event in Saskatoon, Saskatchewan, Canada, beating Ric Flair.

He was once in a tag team with his brother-in-law, Jim "The Anvil" Neidhart. They were called The Hart Foundation and won the World Tag Team Championship twice!

After a long absence, Hart returned to WWE in 2010 and finally defeated his biggest rival, Mr. McMahon, with help from many members of his family.

Nickname: The Excellence of Execution

Height: 6 ft

Weight: 235 lbs

Hometown: Calgary, Alberta, Canada

Signature Moves: The Sharpshooter; Hart Attack

Career Highlights: WWE Champion; Intercontinental Champion; World Tag Team Champion; King of the Ring; two-time Royal Rumble Match winner; United States Champion; WCW Tag Team Champion; WCW Champion; Raw General Manager; Two-time WWE Hall of Fame Inductee (Class of 2006 & 2019)

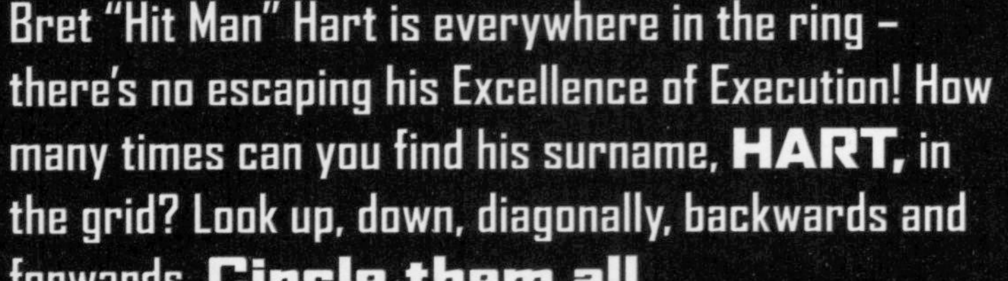

Bret "Hit Man" Hart is everywhere in the ring – there's no escaping his Excellence of Execution! How many times can you find his surname, **HART,** in the grid? Look up, down, diagonally, backwards and forwards. **Circle them all.**

H	T	H	A	R	T
T	H	A	R	T	R
T	R	R	H	R	A
R	A	T	R	A	H
A	H	A	R	T	A
H	A	R	T	T	R

REVEAL THE AWESOMENESS

Cross out every **W** and **M** below to reveal another nickname used for the legendary **Bret "Hit Man" Hart**.

W	M	W	M	T	M	W	M	W	M
M	W	H	W	M	W	M	W	M	E
W	W	M	W	W	M	W	W	M	W
M	W	B	M	W	W	M	E	W	M
S	M	M	W	T	W	M	W	M	W
M	W	M	W	M	M	W	W	T	W
W	M	H	W	M	W	M	W	M	M
M	W	M	W	E	M	W	M	R	W
W	M	W	W	W	M	E	W	M	M
M	W	M	I	W	M	W	W	S	W

CATCHPHRASE:
"I'M THE BEST THERE IS, THE BEST THERE WAS, AND THE BEST THERE EVER WILL BE."

_ _ _ _   _ _ _ _ _

_ _ _ _ _ _ _ _   _ _

Now cross out every **B** and **D** in this grid to reveal the name of one of **Hit Man's biggest rivals.**

B	B	D	B	D	D	B	D	B	D
B	D	B	D	D	B	D	A	D	B
D	M	D	S	B	D	B	B	D	B
E	D	B	D	B	D	B	D	I	D
D	B	B	D	B	D	D	B	D	B
H	D	B	B	D	B	B	L	D	B
B	D	B	C	D	N	D	B	B	D
B	A	B	D	B	D	D	B	S	B
B	D	B	D	B	D	D	B	D	B
W	B	D	B	D	D	B	D	B	H

_ _ _ _ _

_ _ _ _ _ _ _ _

ANSWERS: ON PAGE 77

RANDY SAVAGE

||| His entrance music was called "Pomp and Circumstance" – totally suiting his style! |||

||| Before he became "Macho Man" he debuted in 1973 as a character named "The Spider". |||

||| "Macho Man" almost became a Major League Baseball player, but an injury to his arm meant he switched to WWE instead. |||

Nickname: Macho Man

Height: 6 ft 2 inches

Weight: 237 lbs

Hometown: Sarasota, Florida, United States

Signature Move: Elbow drop off the top rope

Career Highlights: WWE Champion, World Heavyweight Champion, Intercontinental Champion, married Miss Elizabeth at SummerSlam 1991, 2015 WWE Hall of Fame Inductee

Answer the clues to **fill in this word grid.** Once you've finished, Macho Man's hometown will be revealed in the centre column.

1. Macho Man's original nickname was The ______. [6]
2. What is Macho Man's last name? [6]
3. What is his first name? [5]
4. What sport did he play before entering WWE? [8]
5. Macho Man called himself the "____ there is". [4]
6. His signature move is the "_____ drop of the top rope". [5]
7. He was "too ___ to handle". [3]
8. His home country was the United ______. [6]

1
2
3
4
5
6
7
8

MACHO MAZE!

Oooh yeah! Macho Man is on his way to the ring to defeat his rival, but which path will get him there?

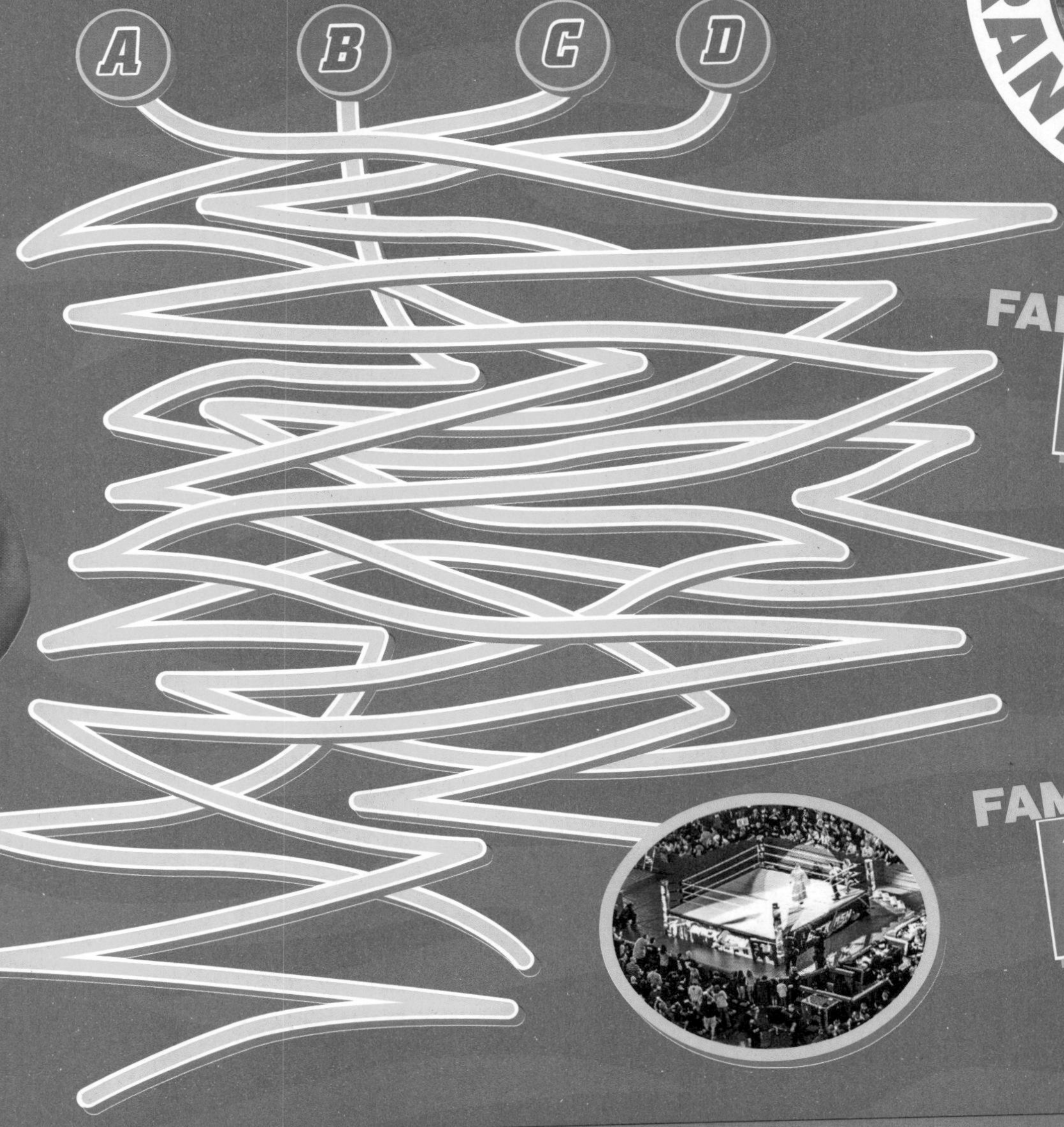

A B C D

MACHO MAN RANDY SAVAGE

FAMOUS QUOTES:

"Too hot to handle, too cold to hold!"

FAMOUS QUOTES:

"Best there is ... past, present and future! Ooooh yeeeah!"

Can you spot **6 differences** between these two pictures? **Circle them all!**

ANSWERS: ON PAGE 77

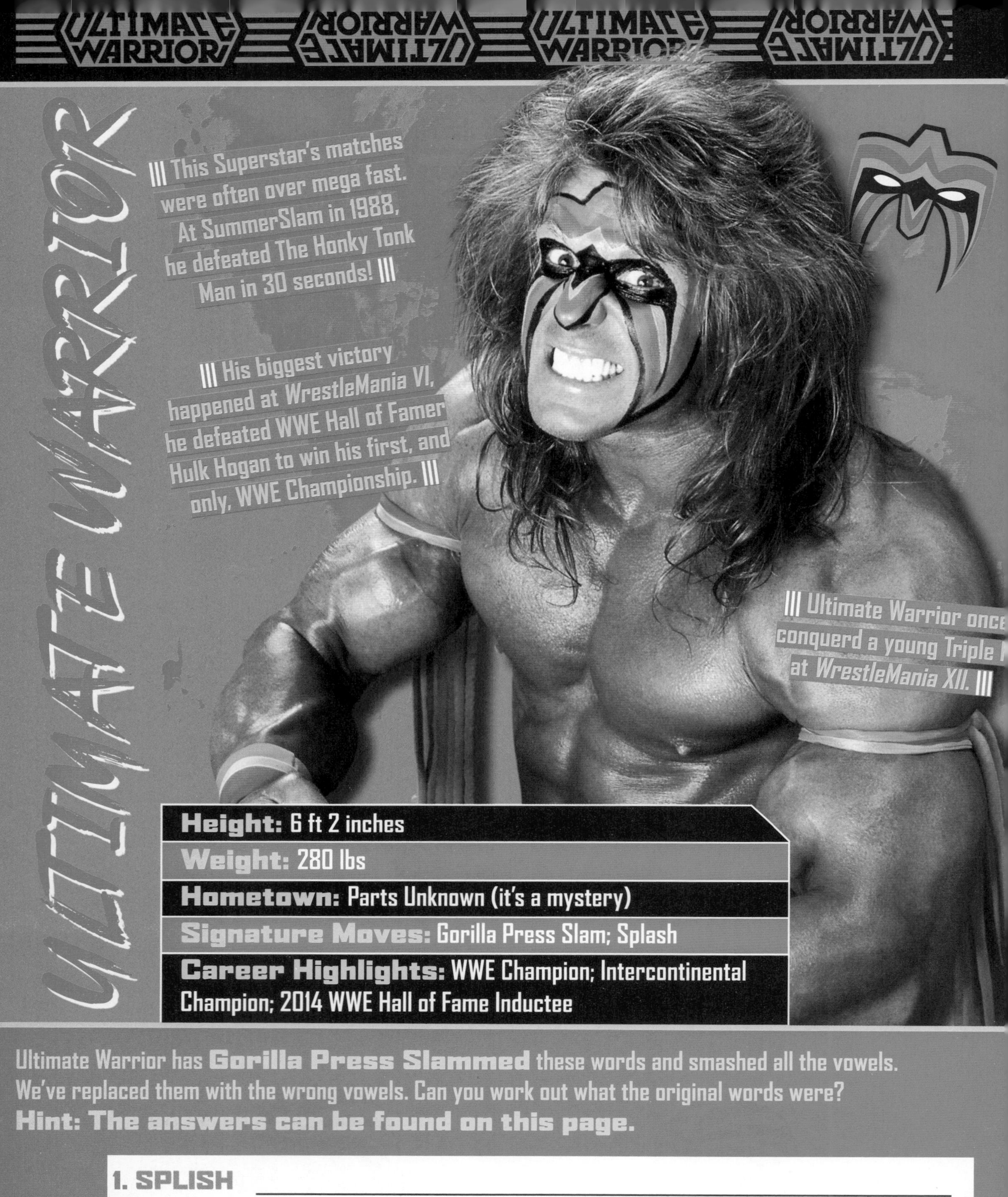

ULTIMATE WARRIOR

This Superstar's matches were often over mega fast. At SummerSlam in 1988, he defeated The Honky Tonk Man in 30 seconds!

His biggest victory happened at WrestleMania VI, he defeated WWE Hall of Famer Hulk Hogan to win his first, and only, WWE Championship.

Ultimate Warrior once conquerd a young Triple H at WrestleMania XII.

Height: 6 ft 2 inches

Weight: 280 lbs

Hometown: Parts Unknown (it's a mystery)

Signature Moves: Gorilla Press Slam; Splash

Career Highlights: WWE Champion; Intercontinental Champion; 2014 WWE Hall of Fame Inductee

Ultimate Warrior has **Gorilla Press Slammed** these words and smashed all the vowels. We've replaced them with the wrong vowels. Can you work out what the original words were? **Hint: The answers can be found on this page.**

1. SPLISH ______
2. WORRAUR ______
3. ALTOMETO ______
4. PORTS INKNAWN ______
5. WROSTLAMONEU ______

MAKE YOUR MASK

Ultimate Warrior famously hid his face under a painted mask and spoke in a cryptic way – always hiding his true identity. Design your own warrior mask – and **make it wild**! You can try out four different mask designs on this page.

ANSWERS: ON PAGE 77

FAMOUS QUOTES:

"There is no place to run! All the fuses in the exit signs have been burnt out!"

"Come on in where nightmares are the best part of my day!"

"Load up the spaceship with the rocket fuel!"

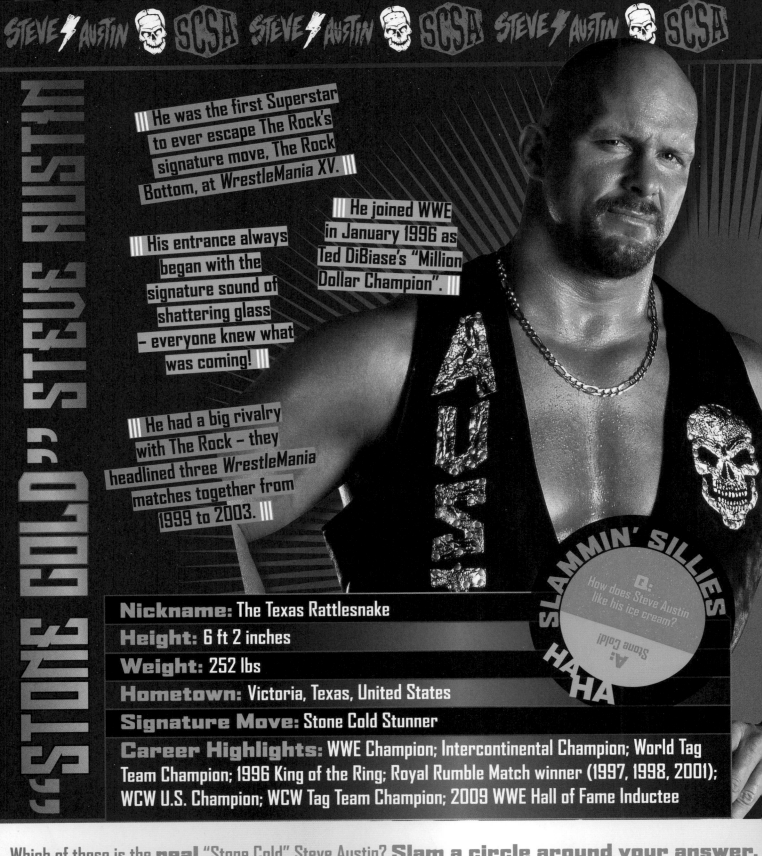

"STONE COLD" STEVE AUSTIN

He was the first Superstar to ever escape The Rock's signature move, The Rock Bottom, at *WrestleMania XV*.

He joined WWE in January 1996 as Ted DiBiase's "Million Dollar Champion".

His entrance always began with the signature sound of shattering glass – everyone knew what was coming!

He had a big rivalry with The Rock – they headlined three *WrestleMania* matches together from 1999 to 2003.

SLAMMIN' SILLIES

Q: How does Steve Austin like his ice cream?

A: Stone Cold!

HAHAHA

Nickname: The Texas Rattlesnake

Height: 6 ft 2 inches

Weight: 252 lbs

Hometown: Victoria, Texas, United States

Signature Move: Stone Cold Stunner

Career Highlights: WWE Champion; Intercontinental Champion; World Tag Team Champion; 1996 King of the Ring; Royal Rumble Match winner (1997, 1998, 2001); WCW U.S. Champion; WCW Tag Team Champion; 2009 WWE Hall of Fame Inductee

Which of these is the **real** "Stone Cold" Steve Austin? **Slam a circle around your answer.**

1

2

3

'COS STONE COLD SAID SO!

"Stone Cold" is famous for getting people to do things "because he said so. "But which of these quotes did the legendary Superstar **actually** say? Tick the ones you think are right, then check the answer page.

1 *"I can drive anything on wheels... I can drive anything, actually."*

2 *"With drive and a bit of talent you can move mountains."*

3 *"Live strong, act bold, be brave. Nothing's hard to do, ALWAYS BELIEVE."*

4 *"I eat so much chicken, I'm surprised I haven't grown feathers yet."*

5 *"Tune in next week, same Stone Cold time, same Stone Cold channel."*

6 *"Nobody remembers second place"*

7 *"If your goal isn't to be on top, then you don't deserve to be here."*

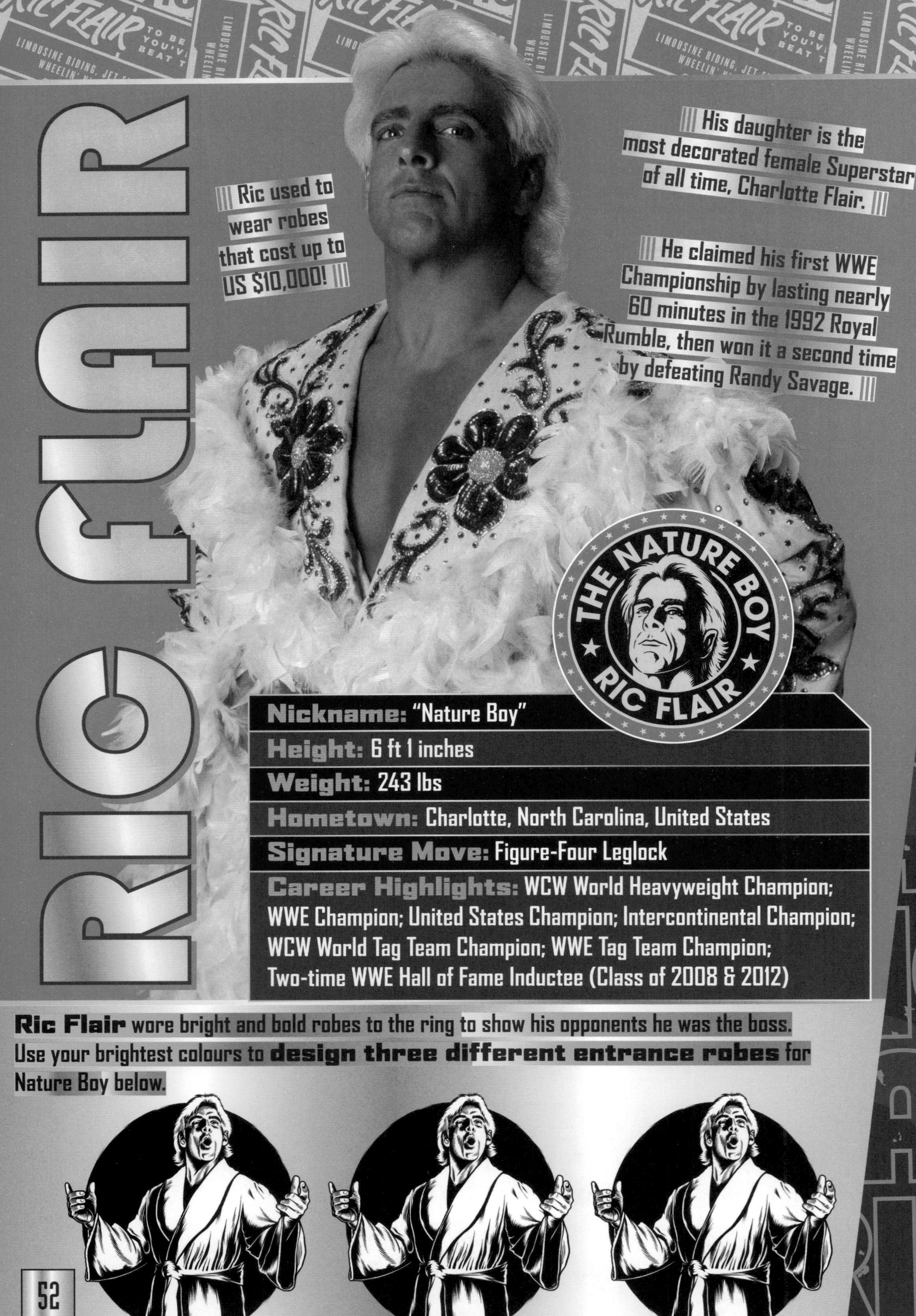

RIC FLAIR

Ric used to wear robes that cost up to US $10,000!

His daughter is the most decorated female Superstar of all time, Charlotte Flair.

He claimed his first WWE Championship by lasting nearly 60 minutes in the 1992 Royal Rumble, then won it a second time by defeating Randy Savage.

Nickname: "Nature Boy"

Height: 6 ft 1 inches

Weight: 243 lbs

Hometown: Charlotte, North Carolina, United States

Signature Move: Figure-Four Leglock

Career Highlights: WCW World Heavyweight Champion; WWE Champion; United States Champion; Intercontinental Champion; WCW World Tag Team Champion; WWE Tag Team Champion; Two-time WWE Hall of Fame Inductee (Class of 2008 & 2012)

Ric Flair wore bright and bold robes to the ring to show his opponents he was the boss. Use your brightest colours to **design three different entrance robes** for Nature Boy below.

DIAMONDS ARE FOREVER – AND SO IS RIC FLAIR!

Ric Flair was famous for his **outrageous outfits** and **expensive attire**. Help him count his diamonds!

1 + = ____

2 + = ____

3 + = ____

4 + = ____

5 + = ____

6 + = ____

7 + = ____

8 + = ____

FAMOUS QUOTES:

"Whether you like it or not, learn to love it, because it's the best thing going. Wooooo!"

"My shoes are worth more than your house!"

"I'm gonna walk down the aisle in style and profile."

ANSWERS: ON PAGE 77

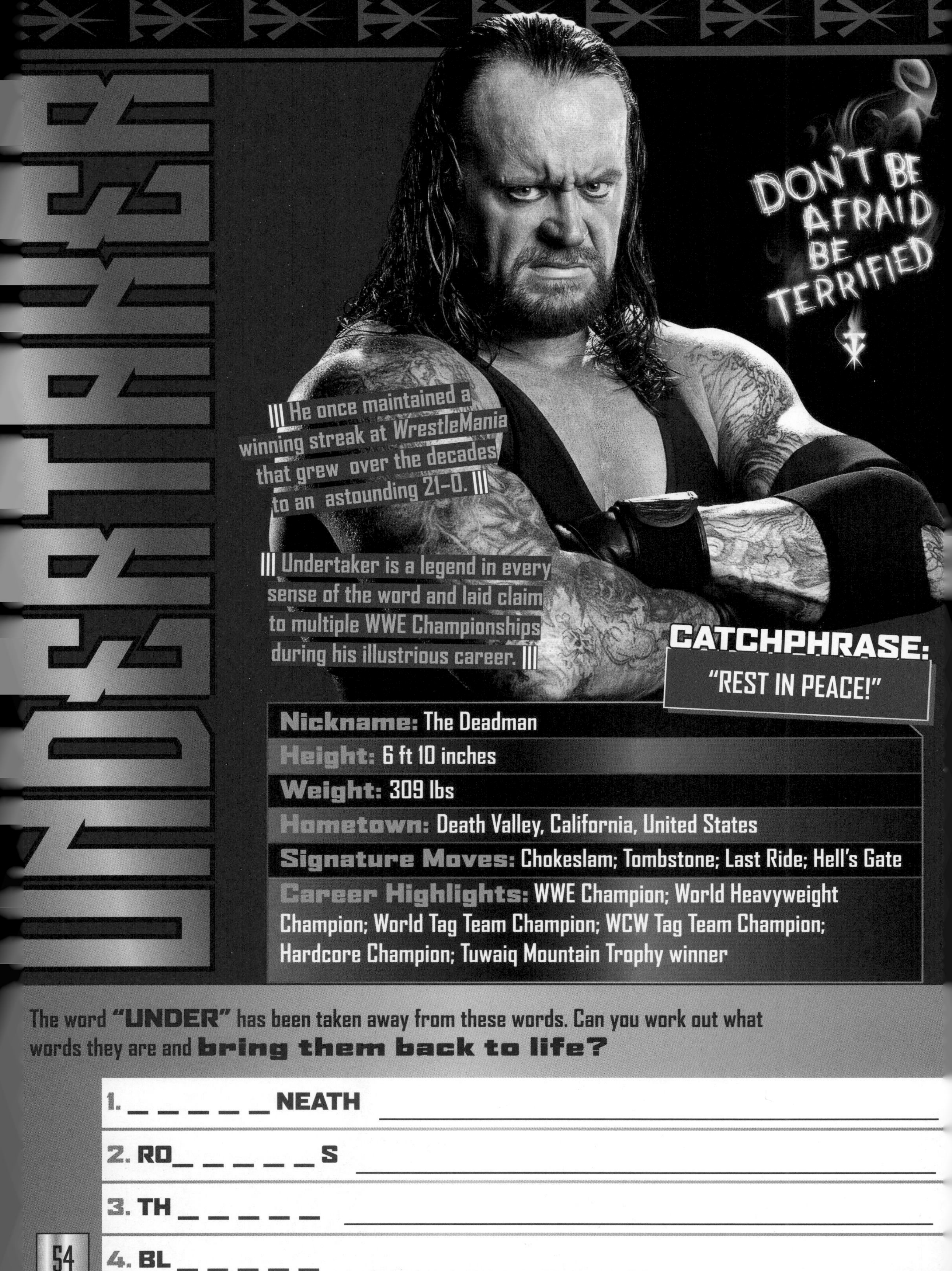

UNDERTAKER
DON'T BE AFRAID BE TERRIFIED
He once maintained a winning streak at WrestleMania that grew over the decades to an astounding 21-0.
Undertaker is a legend in every sense of the word and laid claim to multiple WWE Championships during his illustrious career.
CATCHPHRASE:
"REST IN PEACE!"
Nickname: The Deadman
Height: 6 ft 10 inches
Weight: 309 lbs
Hometown: Death Valley, California, United States
Signature Moves: Chokeslam; Tombstone; Last Ride; Hell's Gate
Career Highlights: WWE Champion; World Heavyweight Champion; World Tag Team Champion; WCW Tag Team Champion; Hardcore Champion; Tuwaiq Mountain Trophy winner

The word **"UNDER"** has been taken away from these words. Can you work out what words they are and **bring them back to life?**

1. _ _ _ _ _ NEATH ______________________

2. RO_ _ _ _ _ S ______________________

3. TH _ _ _ _ _ ______________________

4. BL _ _ _ _ _ ______________________

TRUE OR FALSE

Undertaker is a menacing, mysterious legend of the ring. Can you work out which of these statements about him are true and which are totally false? Circle your answers.

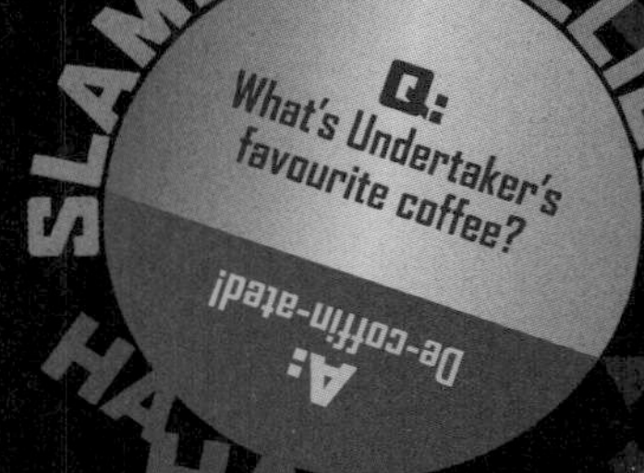

1. HE WAS FIRST INTRODUCED AT 1990's SURVIVOR SERIES — TRUE / FALSE
2. HIS NAME WAS ONCE KANE THE UNDERTAKER — TRUE / FALSE
3. HIS SIGNATURE MOVE WAS SWEET CHIN MUSIC — TRUE / FALSE
4. HE WAS BORN IN 1985 — TRUE / FALSE
5. HIS ASTOUNDING CAREER CAME TO AN END WHEN HE RETIRED IN 2020 — TRUE / FALSE
6. HE IS OVER 7 FEET TALL — TRUE / FALSE
7. HIS HOMETOWN IS DEATH VALLEY — TRUE / FALSE
8. HE HAS THREE SIGNATURE MOVES — TRUE / FALSE
9. HIS NICKNAME IS THE DEADMAN — TRUE / FALSE
10. HE IS ALSO SOMETIMES KNOWN AS THE PHENOM — TRUE / FALSE

ANSWERS: ON PAGE 77

SHAWN MICHAELS

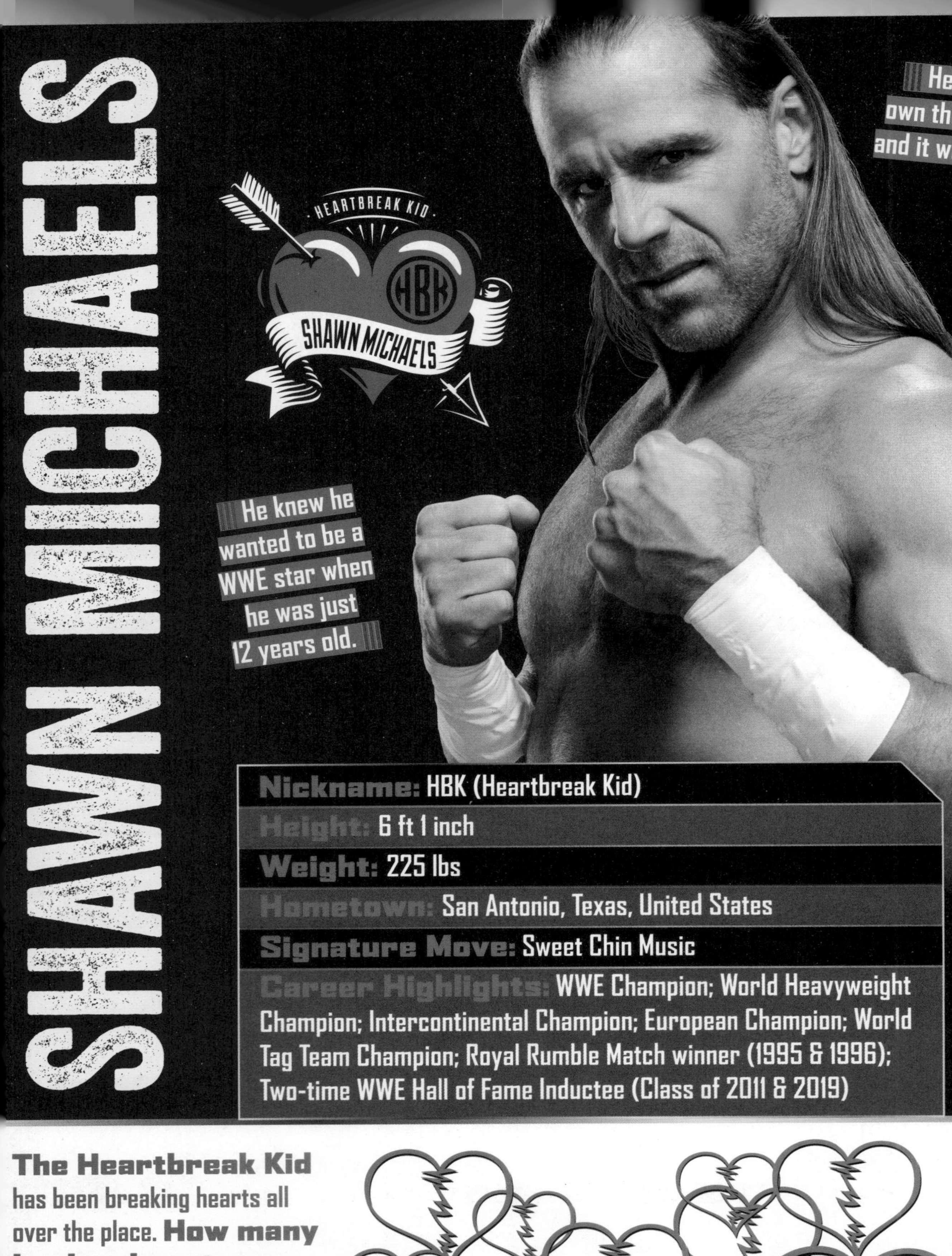

He wrote his own theme song – and it was iconic!

He knew he wanted to be a WWE star when he was just 12 years old.

Nickname: HBK (Heartbreak Kid)
Height: 6 ft 1 inch
Weight: 225 lbs
Hometown: San Antonio, Texas, United States
Signature Move: Sweet Chin Music
Career Highlights: WWE Champion; World Heavyweight Champion; Intercontinental Champion; European Champion; World Tag Team Champion; Royal Rumble Match winner (1995 & 1996); Two-time WWE Hall of Fame Inductee (Class of 2011 & 2019)

The Heartbreak Kid has been breaking hearts all over the place. **How many broken hearts can you count?**

THE ICON, THE SHOWSTOPPER, THE MAIN EVENT

Colour this **showstopping** picture of The Heartbreak Kid in action in the ring.

THE HEARTBREAK KID
SHAWN MICHAELS

SLAMMIN' SILLIES

Q: What is Shawn Michaels' favourite thing to listen to?

A: Sweet Chin Music!

HA HA

ANSWERS: ON PAGE 77

DEFEAT *THE* DIFFERENCES

Superstars Danie[illegible] Sami Zayn face e[illegible] once again in the ring! Can you fin[illegible] **10 differen[illegible]** two pictures bel[illegible]

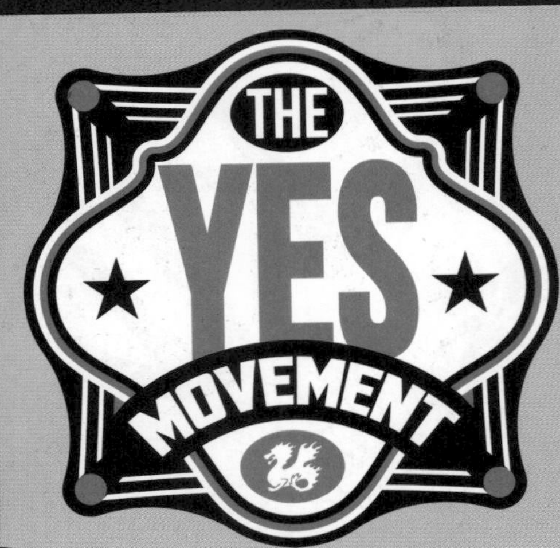

1 V'S

2 V'S

Sami Zayn defeated Daniel Bryan on Night 1 of *WrestleMania 36* to retain the Intercontinental Championship!

Bryan attempted an attack off the top rope, but Zayn countered into a modified version of Helluva Kick for the win.

DEFEAT THE DIFFERENCES

Bianca Belair takes on Bayley in an epic match! Can you spot **10 differences** in the second picture below?

1

KNOW YOUR ROLE... MODEL
BAY LEY
VS

2

KNOW YOUR ROLE... MODEL
BEY LEY
VS

The powerful pair met in a mighty SmackDown match in January 2021.

Bayley held Bianca in a tabletop cover, but Bianca broke out and issued her new finisher, the Kiss of Death. She covered Bayley to claim the win.

ANSWERS: ON PAGE 77

MILLION DOLLAR MATHS

Legendary Superstar "Million Dollar Man" Ted DiBiase had a fortune to beat any rival. Can you help him add up his dollars by filling in the missing numbers in these two pyramids? The number in each space is the total of the two numbers below it.

112

28

4 7 10

3 5 4

Ted DiBiase conquered opponents with his signature move, the Million Dollar Dream.

"Million Dollar Man" was in an awesome tag team with Andre the Giant – they were called "The Mega Bucks"

MAZE OF MAYHEM!

A Superstar's big entrance is the ultimate way to **intimidate** their opponent. Can you make an entrance to remember? Find your way through the maze to the ring!

Think about your ultimate Superstar entrance and fill in the details below!

MY ENTRANCE SONG WOULD BE: ....

I WOULD GET TO THE RING BY: ....

I WOULD INTIMIDATE MY OPPONENTS BY: ....

I WOULD BE WEARING: ....

ANSWERS: ON PAGE 77

ICONIC

Do you know the Superstar names of these WWE icons? Write the correct name for each Superstar under their image.

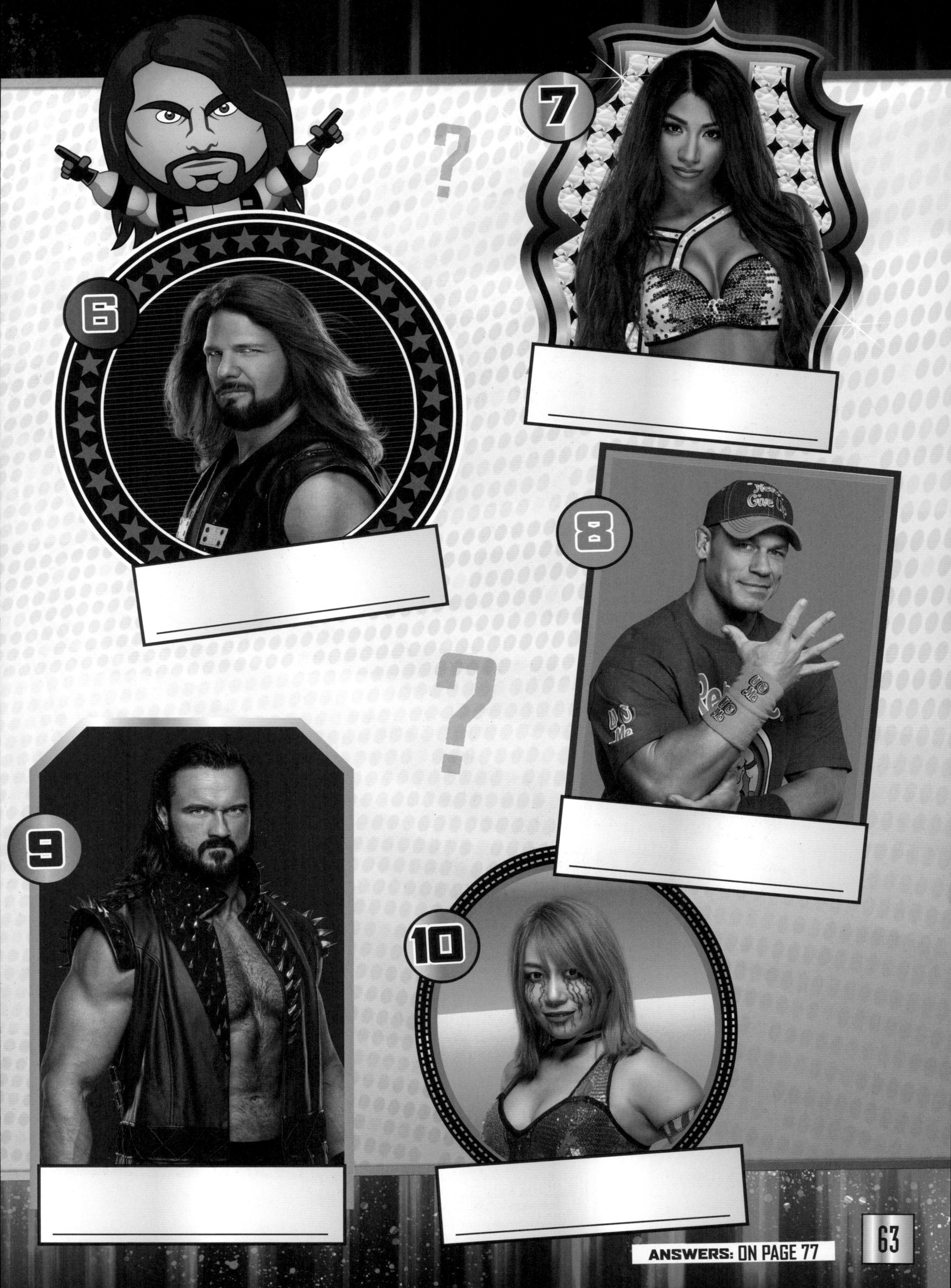

ANSWERS: ON PAGE 77

FEARSOME FAMILY

Superstars **Roman Reigns** and **The Usos (Jey and Jimmy)** make up a terrifying tag team. Can you work out which jigsaw piece is the correct one to complete the picture?

||| All three Superstars are members of the Anoa'i family. |||

||| Reigns is the son of another Hall-of-Famer, Sika. |||

||| The Usos are the sons of Hall-of-Famer Rikishi. |||

||| Reigns and The Usos are first cousins once removed. |||

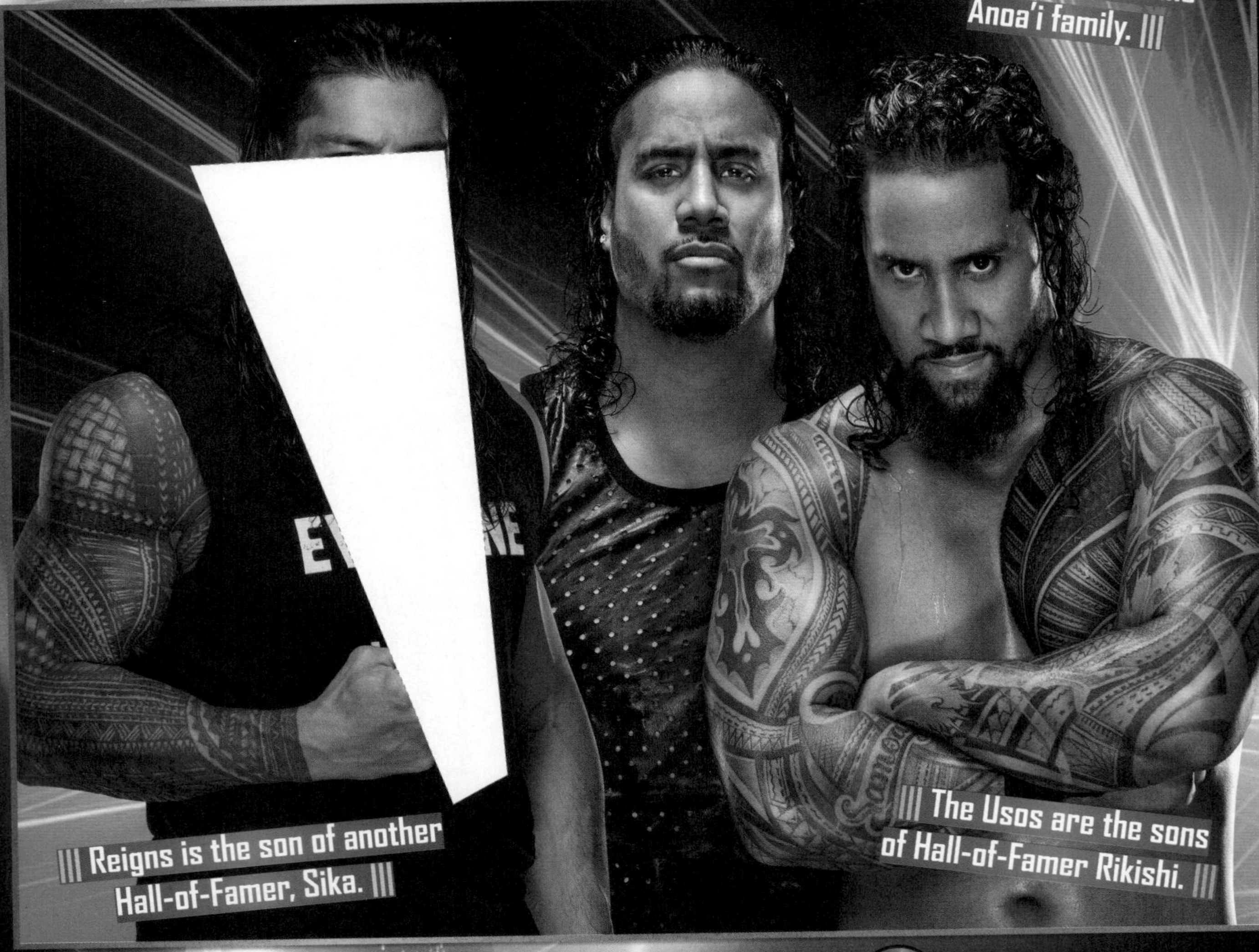

MEMORY MATCH

It's time to put your memory to the test. Take a few minutes to study the picture and facts on the previous page, then cover it up and **answer the questions below** – without cheating!

ROMAN EMPIRE

1 DOES ROMAN REIGNS HAVE A BEARD?

2 WHICH OF ROMAN'S ARMS IS TATTOOED?

3 WHICH OF THE USOS IS WEARING A VEST TOP?

4 IS ROMAN'S HAIR TIED UP OR HANGING LOOSE?

5 IS ROMAN STANDING IN THE MIDDLE?

6 ARE REIGNS AND THE USOS FIRST COUSINS TWICE REMOVED?

7 WHAT FAMILY DO ALL THREE SUPERSTARS BELONG TO?

8 WHAT IS THE NAME OF ROMAN REIGNS' FATHER?

9 WHAT IS THE NAME OF THE USOS' FATHER?

ANSWERS: ON PAGE 77

THE QUIZ OF LEGENDS

The Superstars on these pages are the most legendary in WWE history. How well do you know them? Answer each statement by ticking **TRUE** or **FALSE**.

1
Bret "Hit Man" Hart's signature move is The Sharpshooter.
TRUE
FALSE
BRET HART
HIT MAN
2
"Macho Man" is the nickname for Shawn Michaels.
MACHO MAN
TRUE
FALSE
3
Andre The Giant is over 7 feet tall.
TRUE
FALSE
ANDRE GIANT
4
"Rowdy" Roddy Piper is from Glasgow in Scotland.
TRUE
FALSE
HOT ROD
ROWDY RODDY PIPER

5
"Nature Boy" Ric Flair's daughter is Alexa Bliss.
TRUE
FALSE
RIC FLAIR
The Nature Boy
6
Shawn Michaels' once wrote his own theme tune.
TRUE
FALSE
SHOW
STOPP
HEART
7
Ted Dibiase is better known as "Billion Dollar Man".
TRUE
FALSE
8
"Stone Cold" Steve Austin joined WWE in 2016.
AUSTIN 3:16
STONE COLD
TRUE
FALSE
9
Razor Ramon is also know as "The Good Guy".
TRUE
FALSE
10
Sgt. Slaughter's signature move was the Cobra Clutch.
TRUE
FALSE
ANSWERS: ON PAGE 77

FINISH IT!

Your knockout skills are needed to finish the sequence in each row below. Use your stickers to complete them. **Draw the symbol that comes next in each row.**

1 

2 

3 

4 

5 

6 

HIDDEN HERO

There's a name of a WWE **ICON** hidden in this puzzle.

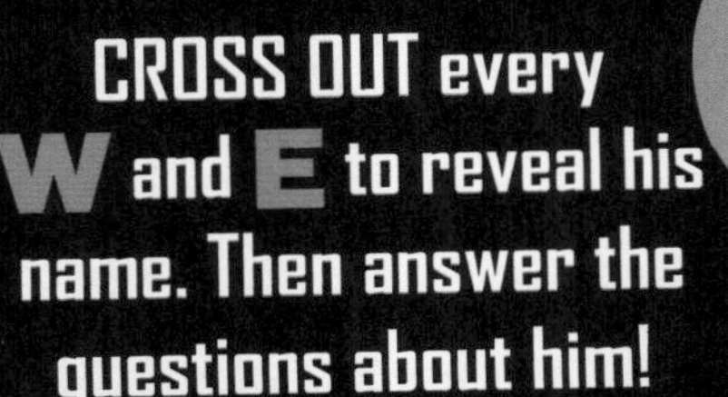

CROSS OUT every **W** and **E** to reveal his name. Then answer the questions about him!

W	W	E	W	W	E	R	W
E	A	W	E	W	W	E	W
W	E	W	W	E	N	W	E
W	D	E	W	W	E	W	W
E	W	W	E	W	W	E	Y
W	E	W	W	E	W	W	E
W	W	E	W	W	E	W	W
E	O	W	E	W	W	E	W
W	E	W	W	R	W	W	E
W	T	E	W	W	E	W	W
E	W	W	E	W	O	E	W
W	E	W	N	E	W	W	E

1. DO YOU KNOW HIS SIGNATURE MOVE?
2. WHAT IS HIS NICKNAME?
3. WHAT IS HIS HOMETOWN?

ANSWERS: ON PAGE 77

THE GREATEST GRID

The gloves are on and it's time to test your **WWE knowledge** with this ultimate crossword. Answer the clues to complete the grid.

ACROSS:

1. NAME OF THE MONDAY NIGHT WWE SHOW. [3]
2. BECKY ______, NICKNAMED THE MAN. [5]
3. NAME OF THE FRIDAY NIGHT WWE SHOW. [9]

DOWN:

1. WHAT IS SUPERSTAR SETH'S LAST NAME? [7]
4. THE FIEND IS THE ALTER-EGO OF BRAY ______. [5]
5. DWAYNE JOHNSON IS BETTER KNOWN AS THE _____. [4]

ANSWERS: ON PAGE 77

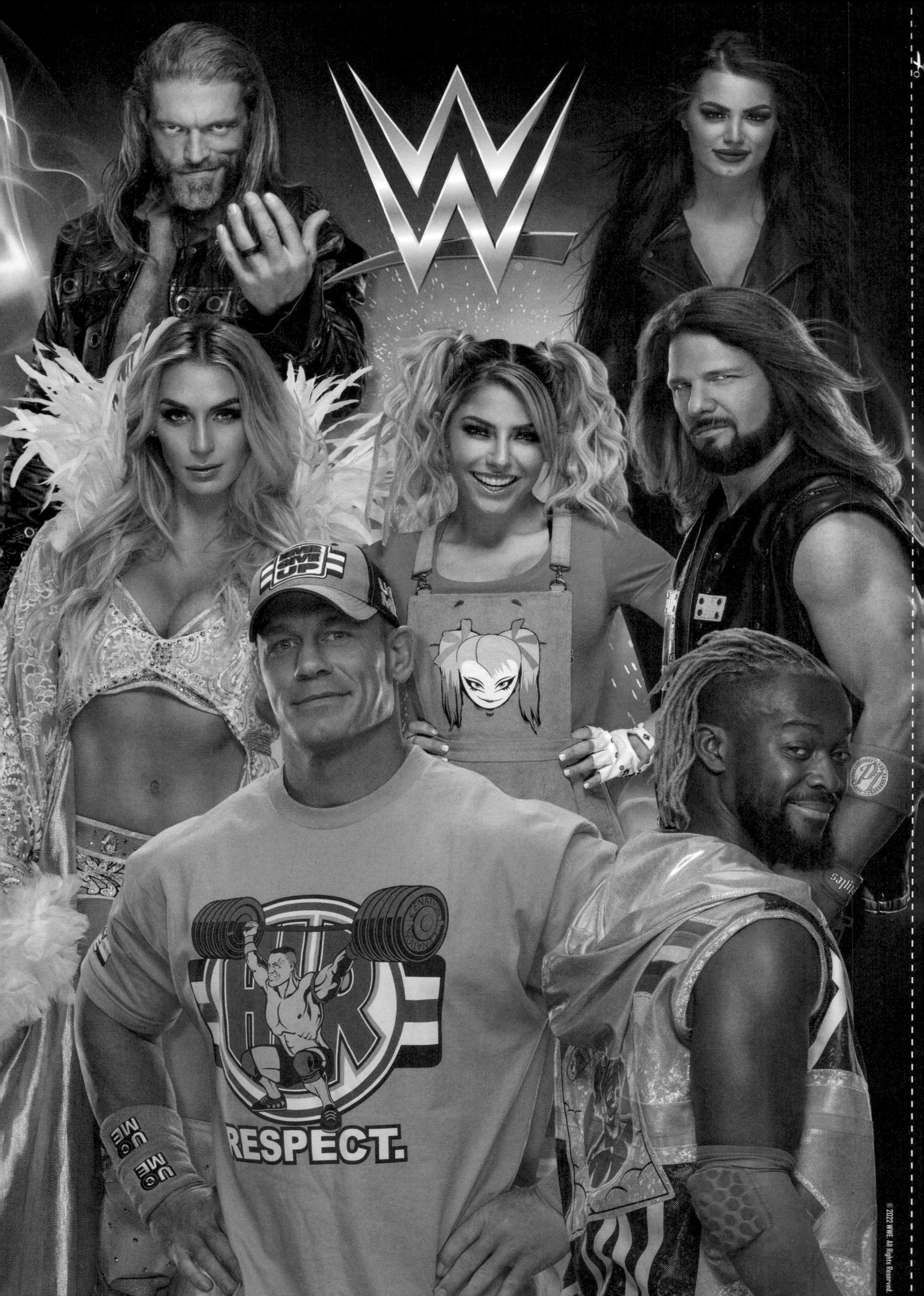
NEVER GIVE UP
RESPECT.

YOUR WWE

Now you've conquered this **slammin' annual,** fill in this page with all your **favourite things** about WWE, and stuff you'd love to see.

Who is your **favourite Superstar?**

Why do they **rock?**

Who would you **love** to see them **conquer** in the ring?

What **moves** would they use to win?

What is your **dream *WrestleMania* line-up?**

Who would you love to see form a **tag team?**

SUPERSTAR YOU!

Imagine yourself as a **WWE Superstar!**

Your **Superstar name:**

Your nickname:

What's your **Superstar personality?**
Are you friendly, fearsome or fun?

Your **signature move** (name it and describe it):

What's your **catchphrase** in the ring?

Draw your
very own logo:

Now draw the Superstar version of you!

Don't forget to match your costume to your awesome personality and name.

ANSWERS

Page 9

1. YOU CAN'T SEE ME,
2. HUSTLE, LOYALTY, RESPECT,
3. NEVER GIVE UP

Page 11

A	L	O	P	D	L	I	A	E	A
S	G	W	P	H	E	I	R	M	O
M	T	H	E	B	I	G	D	O	G
A	F	A	N	O	K	M	T	R	U
C	L	S	S	K	R	A	P	N	K
K	O	N	A	P	Y	O	R	I	N
D	R	G	C	S	M	E	M	V	O
O	I	I	D	L	W	O	K	A	W
W	D	E	L	M	H	D	K	R	N
N	A	R	A	E	P	S	M	A	E

Page 13

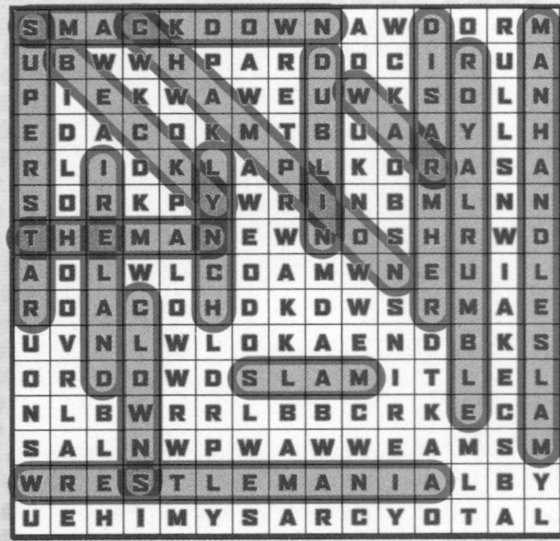

Page 14

1. QUEEN, **2.** LEGLOCK,
3. VOLLEYBALL, **4.** NATURE BOY,
5. CONQUER

Pages 16-17

7 TIMES
4

R	O	C	K	R
O	O	R	C	O
C	K	C	O	R
K	C	R	K	O
K	O	R	K	C
C	R	O	C	K

Page 21

1. ADAM COPELAND, **2.** SMACKDOWN,
3. 1973, **4.** SPEAR, **5.** CANADA
6. KISS, **7.** 6 FT 5 INCHES, **8.** GUITAR,
9. LEATHER, **10.** A NECK INJURY

Pages 22-23

1. BECKY LYNCH, **2.** KOFI KINGSTON
3. TRIPLE H, **4.** THE ROCK
5. BAYLEY, **6.** RANDY ORTON
7. SASHA BANKS, **8.** THE FIEND

Pages 24-25

RIC & CHARLOTTE FLAIR
(FATHER AND DAUGHTER)
THE ROCK & ROMAN REIGNS
(COUSINS)
BRETT HART & NATALYA
(UNCLE AND NIECE)

Pages 26-27

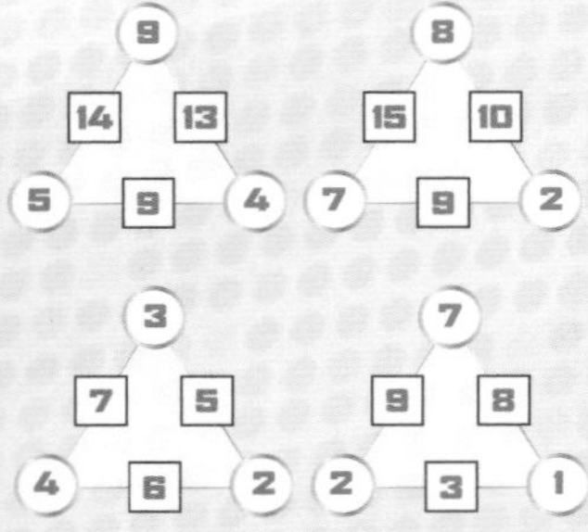

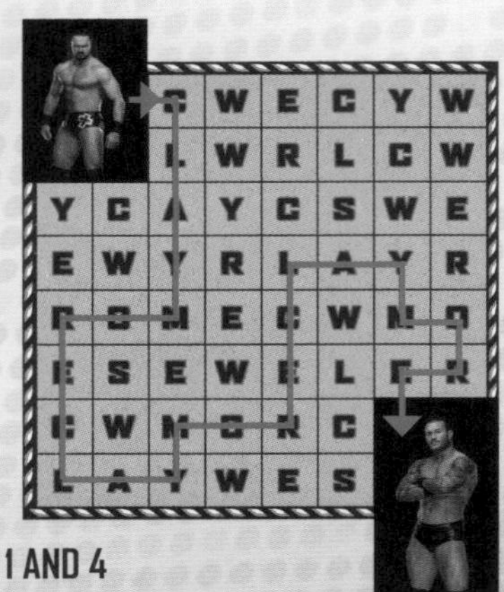

1 AND 4

Page 29

1. JOHN CENA, **2.** ROMAN REIGNS,
3. KANE, **4.** SETH ROLLINS. **5.** BRAUN STROWMAN, **6.** RANDY ORTON,
7. AJ STYLES, **8.** KEVIN OWENS

Pages 32-33

C	A	K	M	D	N	O	W	S
D	W	M	K	O	S	C	N	A
S	N	O	W	A	C	K	D	M
W	M	D	S	N	K	A	C	O
A	O	C	D	W	M	N	S	K
N	K	S	O	C	A	D	M	W
K	S	N	A	M	D	W	O	C
M	C	W	N	K	O	S	A	D
O	D	A	C	S	W	M	K	N

1. SUPERSTARS, **2.** THE NEW DAY,
3. BIG ENDING. **4.** POWER, **5.** TAG TEAM
6. WWE ANNUAL, **7.** UNITED STATES

Pages 34-35

1. SMACKDOWN, **2.** STRONGEST, **3.** KNOXVILLE
1. FALSE, **2.** TRUE, **3.** TRUE, **4.** FALSE,
5. TRUE, **6.** FALSE, **7.** TRUE, **8.** FALSE

Pages 36-37

BROCK LESNAR

W	E	C	A	R	C	H	I	T	E	C	T	W	V	T
A	R	V	I	M	S	C	A	S	P	S	S	S	I	H
S	M	E	S	S	I	A	H	W	M	P	A	P	W	E
C	V	W	S	E	T	H	W	I	O	M	V	M	C	S
H	I	E	C	T	V	C	E	H	T	V	I	V	I	H
A	W	A	R	O	L	L	I	N	S	A	O	A	W	I
M	C	W	W	E	R	E	S	W	W	C	R	C	S	E
P	I	H	C	I	W	W	M	W	C	I	S	I	M	L
I	W	S	C	C	H	E	W	A	V	E	H	E	A	D
O	V	E	W	S	E	A	I	S	N	W	E	W	C	M
N	A	S	L	A	Y	E	R	V	A	I	W	I	K	V
D	A	V	E	N	P	O	R	T	E	I	A	I	D	A
E	U	N	I	V	E	R	S	A	L	R	A	O	O	C
W	C	I	S	I	W	S	C	C	H	E	W	W	W	I
S	M	O	N	E	Y	I	N	T	H	E	B	A	N	K

Page 39

Pages 42-43

1. SMACKDOWN, **2.** UNDERTAKER, **3.** IRELAND,
4. FINN BÁLOR, **5.** RAW, **6.** BECKY LYNCH,
7. ROMAN REIGNS, **8.** CLAYMORE,
9. BRAY WYATT, **10.** "STONE COLD" STEVE AUSTIN

Page 44

8 TIMES
THE BEST THERE IS
SHAWN MICHAELS

H	T	H	A	R	T
T	H	A	R	T	R
T	R	R	H	R	A
R	A	T	R	A	H
A	H	A	R	T	A
H	A	R	T	T	R

Pages 46-47

1 SPIDER
2 SAVAGE
3 RANDY
4 BASEBALL
5 BEST
6 ELBOW
7 HOT
8 STATES

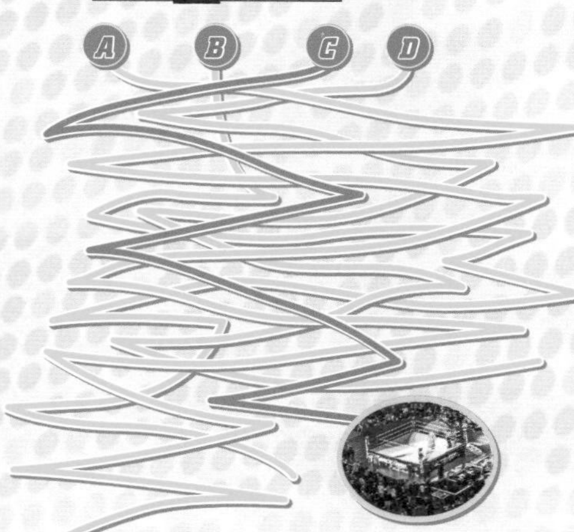

Page 48

1. SPLASH, **2.** WARRIOR,
3. ULTIMATE,
4. PARTS UNKNOWN,
5. WRESTLEMANIA

Pages 50-51

2
1. YES, **2.** NO – THIS WAS SAID BY THE ROCK, **3.** NO – THIS WAS SAID BY ULTIMATE WARRIOR, **4.** YES, **5.** YES **6.** NO – THIS WAS SAID BY JOHN CENA, **7.** NO – THIS WAS SAID BY BIG E

Page 53

1. 4 + 7 = 11, **2.** 5 + 3 = 8,
3. 7 + 7 = 14, **4.** 6 + 9 = 15,
5. 6 + 6 = 12, **6.** 3 + 4 = 7,
7. 5 + 4 = 9, **8.** 9 + 9 = 18

Pages 54-55

1. UNDERNEATH, **2.** ROUNDERS,
3. THUNDER, **4.** BLUNDER
1. TRUE, **2.** TRUE, **3.** FALSE,
4. FALSE – HE WAS BORN IN 1965,
5. TRUE, **6.** FALSE – HE'S 6 FT 10,
7. TRUE, **8.** FALSE – HE HAS FOUR,
9. TRUE, **10.** TRUE.

Pages 56-57

14 broken hearts

Page 58

V'S

Page 59

Page 60

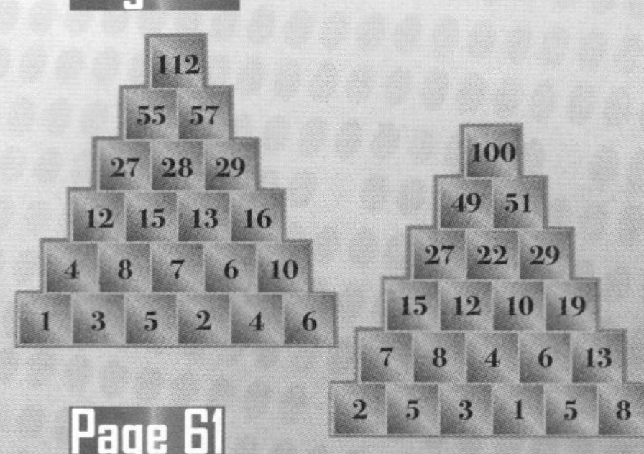

Page 61

Pages 62-63

1. PAIGE, **2.** THE FIEND, **3.** KEITH LEE,
4. ROMAN REIGNS, **5.** BECKY LYNCH,
6. AJ STYLES, **7.** SASHA BANKS,
8. JOHN CENA, **9.** DREW MCINTYRE,
10. ASUKA.

Page 64

PIECE NUMBER 2

Page 65

1. YES, **2.** HIS RIGHT, **3.** JIMMY,
4. HANGING LOOSE, **5.** NO
6. NO, ONCE REMOVED,
7. ANDA'I, **8.** SIKA, **9.** RIKISHI

Pages 66-67

1. TRUE, **2.** FALSE – IT'S RANDY SAVAGE, **3.** TRUE, **4.** TRUE, **5.** FALSE – IT'S CHARLOTTE FLAIR, **6.** FALSE - IT'S MILLION DOLLAR MAN, **7.** TRUE, **8.** FALSE – HE JOINED BACK IN 1996. **9.** FALSE – HE'S THE BAD GUY, **10.** TRUE

Pages 68

1. 2. 3.
4. 5. 6.

Page 69

RANDY ORTON.
1. RKO (RANDY'S KNOCK OUT),
2. THE VIPER, **3.** ST LOUIS, MISSOURI

W	W	E	W	W	E	R	W
E	A	W	E	W	W	E	W
W	E	W	W	E	N	W	E
W	D	E	W	W	E	W	W
E	W	W	E	W	W	E	Y
W	E	W	W	E	W	W	E
W	W	E	W	W	E	W	W
E	O	W	E	W	W	E	W
W	E	W	W	R	W	W	E
W	T	E	W	W	E	W	W
E	W	W	E	W	O	E	W
W	E	W	N	E	W	W	E

Page 70

ACROSS: 1. RAW,
2. LYNCH, **3.** SMACKDOWN.
DOWN: 1. ROLLINS,
4. WYATT, **5.** ROCK